OCR GCSE MATHEMATICS

STAGE 8

GRADUATED ASSESSMENT

AGER

SECOND EDITION

- Howard Baxter
- Michael Handbury
- John Jeskins
- Jean Matthews
- Mark Patmore

Hodder Murray

A MEMBER OF THE HODDER HEADLINE GROUP

The Publishers would like to thank the following for permission to reproduce copyright material:

Photo credits: p.68 (left) © Mark Baigent/Alamy; p.68 (right) © Marc Romanelli/ The Image Bank/ Getty Images.

Acknowledgements Every effort has been made to trace all copyright holders, but if any have been inadvertently overlooked the Publishers will be pleased to make the necessary arrangements at the first opportunity.

Although every effort has been made to ensure that website addresses are correct at time of going to press, Hodder Murray cannot be held responsible for the content of any website mentioned in this book. It is sometimes possible to find a relocated web page by typing in the address of the home page for a website in the URL window of your browser.

Hodder Headline's policy is to use papers that are natural, renewable and recyclable products and made from wood grown in sustainable forests. The logging and manufacturing processes are expected to conform to the environmental regulations of the country of origin.

Orders: please contact Bookpoint Ltd, 130 Milton Park, Abingdon, Oxon OX14 4SB. Telephone: (44) 01235 827720. Fax: (44) 01235 400454. Lines are open from 9 a.m. to 5 p.m., Monday to Saturday, with a 24-hour message-answering service. Visit our website at www.hoddereducation.co.uk.

© Howard Baxter, Michael Handbury, John Jeskins, Jean Matthews, Mark Patmore, Brian Seager, Eddie Wilde, 2006
First published in 2006 by
Hodder Murray, an imprint of Hodder Education,
a member of the Hodder Headline Group
338 Euston Road
London NW1 3BH

Impression number   10 9 8 7 6 5 4 3 2 1
Year   2011 2010 2009 2008 2007 2006

Cover photo © Andy Sacks/Photographer's Choice/Getty Images
Illustrations © Barking Dog Art
Typeset in 10/12 TimesTen by Pantek Arts Ltd, Maidstone, Kent
Printed and bound in Great Britain by CPI Bath

A catalogue record for this title is available from the British Library

ISBN-10: 0340 927 526
ISBN-13: 978 0340 927 526

Contents

STAGE
8

STAGE
8

Introduction

About this book

This course has been written especially for students following OCR's 2006 Modular Specification C, Graduated Assessment (J516) for GCSE Mathematics.

This book covers the complete specification for Stage 8.

- Each chapter is presented in a way which will help you to understand the mathematics, with straightforward explanations and worked examples covering every type of problem.
- At the start of each chapter are two lists, one of what you should already know before you begin and the other of the topics you will be learning about in that chapter.
- 'Activities' offer a more interesting approach to the core content, giving opportunities for you to develop your skills.
- 'Challenges' are rather more searching and are designed to make you think mathematically.
- There are plenty of exercises to work through to practise your skills.
- Some questions are designed to be done without a calculator, so that you can practise for the non-calculator section of the examination papers.
- Look out for the 'Exam tips' – these give advice on how to improve your performance in the module test, direct from the experienced examiners who have written this book.
- At the end of each chapter there is a short summary of what you have learned.
- Finally, there are 'Revision exercises' at intervals throughout the book to help you revise all the topics covered in the preceding chapters.

Other components in the series

- A Homework Book
  This contains parallel exercises to those in this book to give you more practice. Included with the Homework Book is a Personal Tutor CD-ROM. This will help you if you have to miss a lesson or if you need a reminder of something taught in class.
- An Assessment Pack
  There are two Assessment Packs: one for Foundation Tier (Stages 1 to 7) and one for Higher Tier (Stages 6 to 10). Each contains revision exercises, practice module papers and a practice terminal paper to help you prepare for the examination. Some of the questions in the examination will offer you little help to get started. These are called 'unstructured' or 'multi-step' questions. Instead of the question having several parts, each of which helps you to answer the next, you have to work out the necessary steps to find the answer. There will be examples of this kind of question in the Assessment Pack.

- An Interactive Investigations CD-ROM
  This contains whole-class presentations and individual activities. It helps you understand how you can best use ICT to do your homework and other tasks.

Top ten tips

Here are some general tips from the examiners who wrote this book to help you to do well in your tests and examinations.

Practise
1 **taking time** to work through each question carefully.
2 answering questions **without** a calculator.
3 answering questions which require **explanations**.
4 answering **unstructured** questions.
5 **accurate** drawing and construction.
6 answering questions which **need a calculator**, trying to use it efficiently.
7 **checking answers**, especially for reasonable size and degree of accuracy.
8 making your work **concise** and well laid out.
9 checking that you have **answered the question**.
10 **rounding** numbers, but only at the appropriate stage.

STAGE
8

Fractions

Adding and subtracting mixed numbers

To add or subtract mixed numbers, you deal with the whole numbers first.

EXAMPLE 1

Work out these.

a) $1\frac{1}{4} + 2\frac{1}{2}$ b) $2\frac{3}{5} + 4\frac{2}{3}$

a) $1\frac{1}{4} + 2\frac{1}{2} = 1 + 2 + \frac{1}{4} + \frac{1}{2}$ Add the whole numbers first.

$\qquad\qquad = 3 + \frac{1}{4} + \frac{2}{4}$ Common denominator = 4.

$\qquad\qquad = 3\frac{3}{4}$

b) $2\frac{3}{5} + 4\frac{2}{3} = 6 + \frac{3}{5} + \frac{2}{3}$ Add the whole numbers first.

$\qquad\qquad = 6 + \frac{9}{15} + \frac{10}{15}$ Common denominator = 15.

$\qquad\qquad = 6\frac{19}{15}$ $\frac{19}{15}$ is improper ('top heavy').

$\qquad\qquad = 7\frac{4}{15}$ $\frac{19}{15} = 1\frac{4}{15}$

EXAMPLE 2

Work out these.

a) $3\frac{3}{4} - 1\frac{1}{3}$　　　　**b)** $5\frac{3}{10} - 2\frac{3}{4}$

a) $3\frac{3}{4} - 1\frac{1}{3} = 3 - 1 + \frac{3}{4} - \frac{1}{3}$　　　Subtract the whole numbers first.

$= 2 + \frac{9}{12} - \frac{4}{12}$　　　Common denominator = 12.

$= 2\frac{5}{12}$

In part **b)** there is a slight added difficulty.

b) $5\frac{3}{10} - 2\frac{3}{4} = 5 - 2 + \frac{3}{10} - \frac{3}{4}$　　　Subtract the whole numbers first.

$= 3 + \frac{6}{20} - \frac{15}{20}$　　　Common denominator = 20.

$= 2 + \frac{20}{20} + \frac{6}{20} - \frac{15}{20}$　　　$\frac{6}{20} - \frac{15}{20}$ is negative so take one of the whole

$= 2\frac{11}{20}$　　　numbers and change it to $\frac{20}{20}$.

EXERCISE 1.1

1 Add each of these. Write your answers as simply as possible.

a) $1\frac{1}{3} + 3\frac{1}{4}$　　　　**b)** $1\frac{1}{2} + 2\frac{1}{6}$

c) $3\frac{1}{5} + \frac{7}{10}$　　　　**d)** $1\frac{4}{5} + 2\frac{1}{10}$

e) $1\frac{3}{4} + 4\frac{2}{5}$　　　　**f)** $6\frac{1}{6} + 1\frac{4}{9}$

g) $2\frac{5}{6} + 7\frac{4}{9}$　　　　**h)** $2\frac{4}{7} + 1\frac{2}{3}$

i) $\frac{2}{7} + \frac{1}{2} + \frac{5}{14}$　　　　**j)** $\frac{4}{5} + 1\frac{3}{4} + 2\frac{1}{2}$

k) $1\frac{1}{2} + \frac{3}{4} + 2\frac{3}{8}$　　　　**l)** $6\frac{1}{3} + 1\frac{4}{9} + 1\frac{2}{9}$

2 Subtract each of these. Write your answers as simply as possible.

a) $2\frac{4}{5} - 1\frac{3}{5}$　　　　**b)** $2\frac{2}{3} - 1\frac{1}{6}$

c) $5\frac{3}{8} - 2\frac{1}{4}$　　　　**d)** $3\frac{5}{8} - 1\frac{1}{4}$

e) $3\frac{2}{3} - \frac{1}{2}$　　　　**f)** $2\frac{4}{5} - \frac{1}{2}$

g) $3\frac{2}{5} - 1\frac{3}{4}$　　　　**h)** $4\frac{2}{5} - 1\frac{1}{4}$

i) $5\frac{1}{6} - 3\frac{2}{3}$　　　　**j)** $8\frac{1}{6} - 5\frac{3}{8}$

k) $5\frac{1}{5} - \frac{2}{3}$　　　　**l)** $1\frac{1}{4} - \frac{5}{8}$

3 There were three books in a pile on Faisal's desk.
The first book was $2\frac{3}{4}$ inches high, the second $\frac{7}{8}$ inch high and the third $1\frac{5}{6}$ inches high.
What was the total height of the pile?

4 The blade of a knife was $5\frac{3}{4}$ inches long.
The handle was $4\frac{2}{5}$ inches long.
What was the total length of the knife?

5 Caroline bought a piece of ribbon 24 inches long. She cut off two pieces, each $5\frac{5}{8}$ inches long.
How long was the piece she had left?

6 Sam had a piece of wood $28\frac{1}{2}$ inches long.
After using some, $9\frac{5}{8}$ inches were left.
What length did he use?

Multiplying and dividing mixed numbers

To multiply and divide mixed numbers, the mixed numbers must first be changed into improper fractions.

EXAMPLE 3

Work out these.

a) $2\frac{1}{2} \times 4\frac{3}{5}$ **b)** $2\frac{3}{4} \div 1\frac{5}{8}$

a) $2\frac{1}{2} \times 4\frac{3}{5} = \frac{5}{2} \times \frac{23}{5}$ First change the mixed numbers into improper fractions.

$\qquad = \frac{\cancel{5}^1}{2} \times \frac{23}{\cancel{5}_1}$ The arithmetic is much easier if you cancel the 5s.

$\qquad = \frac{23}{2}$ Multiply the numerators and multiply the denominators.

$\qquad = 11\frac{1}{2}$ Change the result back to a mixed number.

b) $2\frac{3}{4} \div 1\frac{5}{8} = \frac{11}{4} \div \frac{13}{8}$ Change the mixed numbers to improper fractions.

$\qquad = \frac{11}{\cancel{4}_1} \times \frac{\cancel{8}^2}{13}$ Invert the second fraction and multiply.

$\qquad$ The arithmetic is much easier if you cancel the 4s.

$\qquad = \frac{22}{13}$ Multiply the numerators and multiply the denominators.

$\qquad = 1\frac{9}{13}$ Change back to a mixed number.

Note that if you are multiplying or dividing by a whole number like 6, you can write it as $\frac{6}{1}$.

EXAM TIP

A common error is to multiply the whole numbers first. Dealing with the whole numbers separately can only be done with addition and subtraction.

EXAM TIP

When cancelling, divide a term in the numerator and a term in the denominator by the same number.

Only cancel a division calculation when it is at the multiplication stage.

STAGE

8

EXERCISE 1.2

Work out these.

1 **a)** $4\frac{1}{2} \times 2\frac{1}{6}$ **b)** $1\frac{1}{2} \times 3\frac{2}{3}$

    c) $4\frac{1}{5} \times 1\frac{2}{3}$ **d)** $3\frac{1}{3} \times 2\frac{2}{5}$

    e) $2\frac{2}{5} \times \frac{3}{4}$ **f)** $3\frac{1}{5} \times 1\frac{2}{3}$

2 **a)** $2\frac{1}{3} \div 1\frac{1}{3}$ **b)** $2\frac{2}{5} \div 1\frac{1}{2}$

    c) $3\frac{1}{5} \div \frac{4}{15}$ **d)** $3\frac{1}{8} \div 1\frac{1}{4}$

    e) $2\frac{1}{4} \div 3\frac{1}{2}$ **f)** $1\frac{1}{5} \div \frac{4}{15}$

3 **a)** $3\frac{1}{2} \times 2\frac{1}{5}$ **b)** $4\frac{2}{7} \times \frac{1}{2}$

    c) $2\frac{3}{4} \div 1\frac{3}{4}$ **d)** $1\frac{5}{12} \div 3\frac{1}{3}$

    e) $3\frac{1}{5} \times 2\frac{5}{8}$ **f)** $2\frac{7}{8} \div 1\frac{3}{4}$

    g) $2\frac{7}{9} \times 3\frac{3}{5}$ **h)** $5\frac{5}{6} \div 1\frac{3}{4}$

    i) $3\frac{5}{7} \times 2\frac{1}{13}$ **j)** $5\frac{2}{5} \div 2\frac{1}{4}$

    k) $5\frac{2}{7} \times 3\frac{1}{2}$ **l)** $4\frac{1}{12} \div 3\frac{1}{4}$

4 **a)** $2\frac{1}{2} \times 1\frac{1}{3} \times 1\frac{3}{8}$ **b)** $1\frac{1}{2} \times 2\frac{2}{3} \div 1\frac{3}{5}$

    c) $1\frac{1}{4} \times 3\frac{1}{5} \div 1\frac{1}{2}$ **d)** $3\frac{1}{2} \times 1\frac{2}{3} \times \frac{5}{7}$

    e) $1\frac{1}{4} \times 1\frac{2}{3} \div 1\frac{1}{9}$ **f)** $3\frac{1}{3} \times 1\frac{1}{4} \div 2\frac{1}{2}$

C CHALLENGE 1

a) Find the perimeter of this rectangle.

b) Find the area of this rectangle.

$5\frac{1}{4}$ cm

$3\frac{2}{3}$ cm

C CHALLENGE 2

Work out these.

a) $\left(3\frac{1}{2} + 2\frac{4}{5}\right) \times 2\frac{1}{12}$ **b)** $5\frac{1}{3} \div 3\frac{3}{5} + 2\frac{1}{3}$

c) $4\frac{2}{3} \times 2\frac{2}{7} - 4\frac{7}{8}$ **d)** $\left(2\frac{4}{5} + 3\frac{1}{4}\right) \div \left(3\frac{2}{3} - 2\frac{3}{4}\right)$

ACTIVITY 1

Fractions on your calculator

You need to be able to calculate with fractions without a calculator. However, when a calculator is allowed you can use the fraction button.

The fraction button looks like this. $\boxed{a^{b/c}}$

To enter a fraction such as $\frac{2}{5}$ into your calculator you press $\boxed{2}$ $\boxed{a^{b/c}}$ $\boxed{5}$ $\boxed{=}$.

Your display will look like this. $\boxed{2 \lrcorner 5}$

This is the calculator's way of showing the fraction $\frac{2}{5}$.

Some calculators may have the $\lrcorner$ symbol a different way round.

To do a calculation like $\frac{2}{5} + \frac{1}{2}$, the sequence of buttons is

$\boxed{2}$ $\boxed{a^{b/c}}$ $\boxed{5}$ $\boxed{+}$ $\boxed{1}$ $\boxed{a^{b/c}}$ $\boxed{2}$ $\boxed{=}$.

This is what you should see on your display.

$\boxed{9 \lrcorner 10}$

You must, of course, write this down as $\frac{9}{10}$ for your answer.

To enter a mixed number such as $2\frac{3}{5}$ into your calculator you press

$\boxed{2}$ $\boxed{a^{b/c}}$ $\boxed{3}$ $\boxed{a^{b/c}}$ $\boxed{5}$ $\boxed{=}$.

Your display will look like this. $\boxed{2 \lrcorner 3 \lrcorner 5}$

You can also cancel a fraction on your calculator.

When you press $\boxed{8}$ $\boxed{a^{b/c}}$ $\boxed{1}$ $\boxed{2}$, you should see $\boxed{8 \lrcorner 12}$.

When you press $\boxed{=}$, the display changes to $\boxed{2 \lrcorner 3}$, meaning $\frac{2}{3}$.

When you do calculations with fractions on your calculator, it will automatically give the answer as a fraction in its lowest terms.

Similarly, if you enter an improper fraction into your calculator and press the $\boxed{=}$ button, the calculator will automatically change it to a mixed number.

Try working through some of the examples and questions earlier in this chapter using your calculator.

STAGE

8

K KEY IDEAS

- When you add or subtract mixed numbers, you deal with the whole numbers first and then the fraction parts.

- To multiply and divide mixed numbers, you must change the mixed numbers to improper ('top heavy') fractions.

Cubic and reciprocal graphs

You will learn about

- Plotting and recognising cubic graphs
- Plotting and recognising reciprocal graphs

You should already know

- How to plot and read points using (x, y) coordinates
- How to substitute numbers into equations

Cubic graphs

EXAMPLE 1

a) Draw the graph of $y = x^3$ for values of x from ⁻3 to 3.
   Label the x-axis from ⁻3 to 3 and the y-axis from ⁻30 to 30.

b) Use your graph to solve the equation $x^3 = 12$.
   Give your answer to 1 decimal place.

a)
x	⁻3	⁻2·5	⁻2	⁻1	0	1	2	2·5	3
y = x³	⁻27	⁻15·6	⁻8	⁻1	0	1	8	15·6	27

The outside points are a long way apart and plotting the values for 2·5 and ⁻2·5 helps with the drawing of the curve.

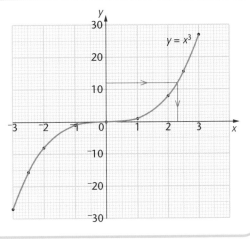

b) To solve $x^3 = 12$, you need to draw across from $y = 12$ to the curve and then down to the x-axis.
Answer $x = 2·3$

Notice the shape of the curve in Example 1. It goes from bottom left to top right and has a 'double bend' in the middle. All cubic curves with a positive x^3 term have a similar shape.

If the x^3 term is negative the curve goes from top left to bottom right.

Notice that the y-scale in Example 1 is not the same as the x-scale. This is because the y-values are much larger than the x-values.

EXAMPLE 2

a) Draw the graph of $y = x^3 - 2x$ for values of x from -2 to 2.
Label the x-axis from -2 to 2 and the y-axis from -4 to 4.

b) Use the graph to solve the equation $x^3 - 2x = 0$.
Give your answers correct to 1 decimal place.

a)

x	-2	-1	-0.5	0	0.5	1	2
x³	-8	-1	-0.125	0	0.125	1	8
- 2x	4	2	1	0	-1	-2	-4
y = x³ - 2x	-4	1	0.875	0	-0.875	-1	4

It helps to see more clearly where the curve is highest and lowest if you work out the values of y for $x = -0.5$ and $x = 0.5$.

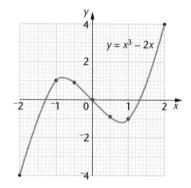

The graph is drawn here with a scale of 1 cm to 1 unit for x and 1 cm to 2 units for y.

b) To solve $x^3 - 2x = 0$, you need to find where $y = x^3 - 2x$ crosses $y = 0$, which is the x-axis.

From the graph, the answers are $x = -1.3$ or 0 or 1.3.

The shape of the curve is similar to the one in Example 1. The $-2x$ term makes the 'double bend' more pronounced.

EXAMPLE 3

Draw the graph of $y = \dfrac{4}{x}$.

x	-4	-3	-2	-1.5	-1	1	1.5	2	3	4
$y = \dfrac{4}{x}$	-1	-1.3	-2	-2.7	-4	4	2.7	2	1.3	1

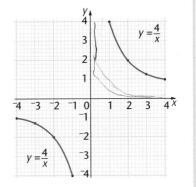

You cannot use 0 as a point in this type of graph, since you cannot divide 4 (or any other number) by 0.

Again it is helpful to work out extra points to give a better curve. In this case you might work out the value of y when $x = {}^{-}1.5$ and 1.5.

It is also useful to have the same scale for both x and y in this case.

All equations of this type $\left(y = \dfrac{a}{x} \text{ where } a \text{ is positive} \right)$ have graphs of the same shape.

There are two separate branches, one in the top right quadrant and one in the bottom left quadrant. Plotting points for $x = 0.5$ and $x = 0.1$ would help to show that the curve gets closer to the axes without ever meeting them.

EXERCISE 2.1

1 **a)** Copy and complete the table for $y = x^3 + 5$.

x	-3	-2	-1	0	1	2	3
x^3	-27			0		8	
+ 5	5						
y	-22						

    b) Draw the graph of $y = x^3 + 5$.
    c) Use your graph to solve the equation $x^3 + 5 = 0$.

2 **a)** Copy and complete the table for $y = x^3 - 4$.

x	-3	-2	-1	0	1	2	3
x^3	-27			0		8	
- 4	-4						
y	-31						

    b) Draw the graph of $y = x^3 - 4$.
    c) Use your graph to solve the equation $x^3 - 4 = 0$.

STAGE

8

EXERCISE 2.1 continued

3 a) Copy and complete the table for $y = {}^-x^3$.

x	$^-3$	$^-2$	$^-1$	0	1	2	3
x^3	$^-27$			0		8	
y	27						

b) Draw the graph of $y = {}^-x^3$.
c) Use your graph to solve the equation $^-x^3 = 6$.

4 a) Draw the graph of $y = 4 - x^3$ for $x = {}^-3$ to $x = 3$.
b) Use your graph to solve the equation $4 - x^3 = {}^-15$.

5 a) Copy and complete the table of values for $y = \dfrac{1}{x}$.

x	$y = \dfrac{1}{x}$
$^-10$	
$^-5$	
$^-2$	
$^-1$	
$^-0.5$	
$^-0.1$	$^-10$
0.1	
0.5	
1	
2	
5	0.2
10	

b) Draw the graph of $y = \dfrac{1}{x}$.
Use a scale of 1 cm to 2 units on both axes.
c) Use your graph to solve each of these.

(i) $\dfrac{1}{x} = 0.3$ **(ii)** $\dfrac{1}{x} = {}^-5$

6 Make a table of values for $y = x^3 - x^2 + 5$, for $x = {}^-2$ to 4. Do not draw the graph.

7 Make a table of values for $y = x^3 - 3x + 4$, for $x = {}^-3$ to 4. Do not draw the graph.

8 Make a table of values for $y = x^3 + 2x^2 - 3$, for $x = {}^-4$ to 2. Do not draw the graph.

9 a) Make a table of values for $y = x^3 - 12x + 2$, for $x = {}^-3$ to 4.
b) Draw the graph of $y = x^3 - 12x + 2$.
c) Solve the equation $x^3 - 12x + 2 = 0$.

10 a) Make a table of values for $y = x^3 - x^2 - 6x$, for $x = {}^-3$ to 4.
b) Draw the graph of $y = x^3 - x^2 - 6x$.
c) Use the graph to solve the equation $x^3 - x^2 - 6x = 0$.

11 a) Make a table of values for $y = \dfrac{8}{x}$, for $x = {}^-8, {}^-4, {}^-2, {}^-1, 1, 2, 4, 8$.
b) Draw the graph of $y = \dfrac{8}{x}$.
Use a scale of 1 cm to 1 unit on both axes.

12 a) Make a table of values for $y = \dfrac{12}{x}$, for $x = {}^-12, {}^-8, {}^-6, {}^-4, {}^-3, {}^-2, {}^-1, 1, 2, 3, 4, 6, 8, 12$.
b) Draw the graph of $y = \dfrac{12}{x}$.

13 **a)** Make a table of values for $y = \dfrac{5}{x}$, for $x = {}^-5, {}^-4, {}^-2.5, {}^-2, {}^-1, 1, 2, 2.5, 4, 5$.

b) Draw the graph of $y = \dfrac{5}{x}$. Use a scale of 1 cm to 1 unit on both axes.

c) On the same grid, draw the graph of $y = x$.

d) Use your graph to solve $x^2 = 5$, giving the answers to 1 decimal place.

> Remember: always make a table of values.

14 **a)** On the same grid, draw the graphs of $y = x^3$ and $y = 5x$, for $x = {}^-3$ to 3.

b) **(i)** Show that when the two curves intersect, the points satisfy the equation $x^3 - 5x = 0$.

(ii) Find the solution to the equation $x^3 - 5x = 0$, giving the answer correct to 1 decimal place.

15 **a)** Draw the graph of $y = x^3 - 3x$, for $x = {}^-3$ to 3.

b) Solve the equation $x^3 - 3x = 0$.

16 **a)** Draw the graph of $y = x^3 - 8x + 12$ for values of x from ${}^-4$ to 3.

b) Use the graph to solve the equation $x^3 - 8x = 0$, giving the answers correct to 1 decimal place.

17 **a)** Draw the graph of $y = x^3 - 4x$ for values of x from ${}^-3$ to 3.

b) Use the graph to solve the equation $x^3 - 4x - 2 = 0$.

18 In this question accurate plotting is *not* required.

a) On the same axes sketch the graphs of $y = x^3$ and $y = \dfrac{10}{x}$.

b) Use your sketch to find out how many solutions there are to the equation $x^3 = \dfrac{10}{x}$.

19 Here are four equations.

a) $y = x^2(x + 5)$

b) $y = x^3$

c) $y = \dfrac{6}{x}$

d) $y = x^3 + 2$

The graphs of these equations are sketched here. They are not in the correct order. State which graph goes with which equation.

(i)

(ii)

(iii)

(iv)

11

C CHALLENGE 1

Here are six equations.

a) $y = 5 - x - x^2$

b) $y = \dfrac{5}{x} + 3$

c) $y = x^3 - 2x - 2$

d) $y = \dfrac{x - 3}{2}$

e) $y = 3x^2 + 2x - 1$

f) $y = 5 + 3x + 2x^2 - x^3$

The graphs of these equations are sketched here but not in the correct order.
Match each graph with the correct equation.

(i)

(ii)

(iii)
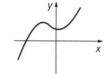

(iv)
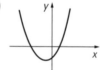

(v)
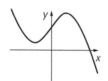

(vi)

KEY IDEAS

■ To draw the graph of a cubic or reciprocal function, first make a table of values.

■ Cubic graphs have the basic shapes shown here.

x^3 term positive

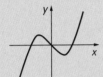

x^3 term negative

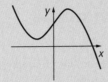

■ Reciprocal graphs are shaped like this.

STAGE
8

3 Probability

You will learn about

- Drawing tree diagrams to represent events
- Calculating the probability of combined events

You should already know

- Probabilities are expressed as fractions or decimals
- All probabilities lie on a scale of 0 to 1
- How to find probability from a set of equally likely outcomes
- The probability of an outcome happening is 1 − the probability of the outcome not happening
- What mutually exclusive events are
- If events A, B and C are mutually exclusive and cover all possible outcomes then $P(A) + P(B) + P(C) = 1$
- How to add, subtract and multiply simple fractions and decimals

Tree diagrams

In this method 'branches' are drawn from a starting point to show the possibilities for the first trial. From the end of each of the first branches, further branches are drawn showing each of the possibilities for the second trial, and so on.

STAGE

8

The tree diagram for tossing two coins looks like this.

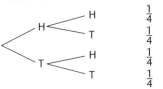

1st coin 2nd coin Probabilities

EXAM TIP

When drawing a tree diagram:
1 allow plenty of space on the page
2 always line up the possibilities for each trial underneath each other
3 for the first trial, draw the branches to points approximately $\frac{1}{4}$ way from the top of your space to $\frac{1}{4}$ way from the bottom of your space.

The probabilities are $\frac{1}{4}$ because there are four equally likely outcomes.

The advantages of a tree diagram are:
- it can easily be extended for a third and subsequent trials
- it can also be used when the outcomes are not equally likely.

The main disadvantage of a tree diagram is that it can look very messy if there are too many possibilities. For example it is difficult to organise in the case of throwing two dice. However, if there are only two or three possible outcomes for each trial it is often the best method.

▋▋ EXAMPLE 1

Fatima throws an ordinary dice and tosses a coin.
Show the possible outcomes on a tree diagram and find the probability that

a) Fatima scores a 6 and a head, which can be written P(6 and head).

b) Fatima scores an odd number and a tail.

a) P(6 and head) = $\frac{1}{12}$ since there are 12 equally likely outcomes.

b) P(odd number and tail) = P[(1, T) or (3, T) or (5, T)] = $\frac{3}{12}$ = $\frac{1}{4}$

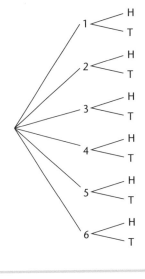

STAGE
8

EXAMPLE 2

Rachel is selecting a main course and a sweet from this menu.

Draw a tree diagram to show Rachel's possible selections.

MENU

Main Course   **Sweet**
Sausage & Chips   Apple Pie
Ham Salad   Fruit Salad
Vegetable Lasagne

If she is equally likely to select any of the choices, what is the probability that she selects Vegetable Lasagne and Apple Pie?

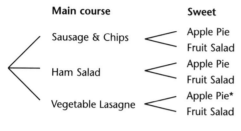

Main course   **Sweet**

Sausage & Chips   Apple Pie
                         Fruit Salad

Ham Salad   Apple Pie
                         Fruit Salad

Vegetable Lasagne   Apple Pie*   *Rachel's Selection
                         Fruit Salad

Therefore there are six possible outcomes.

P(Vegetable Lasagne and Apple Pie) = $\frac{1}{6}$

EXERCISE 3.1

1 Mr and Mrs Green plan to have two children.
Copy and complete the tree diagram for the possible sexes of the children.

1st child   **2nd child**
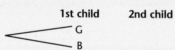
                   G
                   B

Assuming that all outcomes are equally likely, find the probability that
a) both children are girls.
b) Mr and Mrs Green have one child of each sex.

2 Anne tosses three coins.
Draw a tree diagram to show the result of the three tosses.
Find the probability that Anne tosses
a) three heads.
b) two heads and a tail.

3 In tennis one player must win; a draw is not possible. Alex plays three games of tennis against Mike.
Copy and complete the tree diagram to show the possible winners of the games.

1st game   **2nd game**   **3rd game**
                A
                M

Assuming each player is equally likely to win any game, find the probability that
a) Alex wins all three games.
b) Alex wins one and loses two.

4 In a game, Bobbie spins both of these spinners.

Draw a tree diagram showing all the possible outcomes.
What is the probability of getting a B and a 3?

5 Marie takes a sweet from each of two bags without looking.
In the first bag are an equal number of toffees and jelly babies.
In the second bag are an equal number of fruit pastilles, mints and pear drops.
  a) Draw a tree diagram to show the results of Marie's two selections.
  b) What is the probability that she gets a jelly baby and a mint?

6 Mike and Fiona are planning a fundraising event. It will be held in May or June. They are deciding between a sponsored walk or swim or cycle ride. Since they cannot agree they decide to choose randomly.
Copy and complete the tree diagram to show the possible choices.
What is the probability that they choose a walk in June?

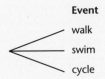

Event	Month
walk	
swim	
cycle	

7 Lisa travels to school by bus or walks, or her mother takes her by car. To go home she either walks or goes by bus.
Copy and complete the tree diagram to show her possible methods of travel.

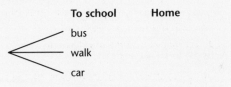

To school	Home
bus	
walk	
car	

If she is equally likely to travel by any of the methods, find the probability that she goes by bus both ways.

8 Asif is choosing his Year 10 options.
In Pool A he can choose Business Studies, ICT or Design.
In Pool B he can choose History, Geography or Economics.
Copy and complete the tree diagram to show his possible choices.
Assuming that he is equally likely to choose any of the subjects, find the probability that Asif chooses ICT and History.

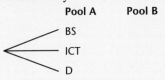

Pool A	Pool B
BS	
ICT	
D	

9 Nicola is choosing from this menu.

MAIN COURSE & SWEET FOR £6·50

Main Course	Sweet
Chicken Chow Mein	Banana Fritter
Sweet & Sour Pork	Ice Cream
Vegetable Curry	

Draw a tree diagram to show her possible choices.
You could use the initial letters, for example CCM, to save you writing the names in full.
Assuming she is equally likely to choose any of the items, find the probability that she chooses Vegetable Curry and Ice Cream.

10 Mr Jones is choosing his new company car. He can choose a Vauxhall or a Ford or a Nissan. He can choose red or blue.
Draw a tree diagram to show his possible choices.
If he chooses randomly, what is the probability that he chooses
  a) a red Ford?
  b) a blue car?

Probability of event A *or* event B happening

Look at the grid for throwing two dice.

Suppose Louise needs a score of 8 or 11. Out of a total of 36 possible outcomes, there are seven that give 8 or 11.

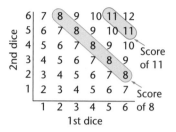

The probability of scoring 8 or 11 is therefore $\frac{7}{36}$.

But the probability of scoring 8 is $\frac{5}{36}$

and the probability of scoring 11 is $\frac{2}{36}$

and $\frac{5}{36} + \frac{2}{36} = \frac{7}{36}$

so P(8 or 11) = P(8) + P(11).

If the two events are 'scoring a double' or 'scoring 8' the situation is different.

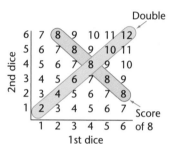

There are ten outcomes that give a double or a score of 8 and therefore:

P(double or 8) = $\frac{10}{36}$.

P(double) = $\frac{6}{36}$

P(8) = $\frac{5}{36}$

but $\frac{6}{36} + \frac{5}{36}$ does not equal $\frac{10}{36}$.

So P(double or 8) does not equal P(double) + P(8).

This is because the events 'scoring a double' and 'scoring 8' are not mutually exclusive events. It is possible to do both by throwing a double 4.

The addition rule only applies to mutually exclusive events.

> **If events A and B are mutually exclusive then P(A or B) = P(A) + P(B).**

STAGE
8

Independent events

If two coins are tossed, the way the first one lands cannot possibly affect the way the second one lands.

Similarly, if two dice are thrown, the way the first one lands cannot possibly affect the way the second one lands.

If there are six red balls and four black balls in a bag, and one is selected and replaced before a second one is selected, the probability of getting a red ball is exactly the same on the second choice as on the first: $\frac{6}{10}$.

> **When an event is unaffected by what has happened in another event, the events are said to be *independent*.**

In the example of six red balls and four black ones, if the first ball is not replaced then the probability of getting a red ball on the second draw is no longer $\frac{6}{10}$ as there are fewer balls in the bag.

> **In this case the events are *dependent*.**

Probability of event A *and* event B happening

In Example 1 Fatima tossed a coin and threw a dice. Since there were 12 equally likely outcomes, and scoring a head and a 6 was one of them, it was concluded that:

P(head and a 6) = $\frac{1}{12}$

Now P(head) = $\frac{1}{2}$ and P(6) = $\frac{1}{6}$

But $\frac{1}{2} \times \frac{1}{6} = \frac{1}{12}$ so P(head and a 6) = P(head) $\times$ P(6)

When two coins are tossed the possible outcomes are (H, H), (H, T), (T, H) and (T, T).

P(two heads) = $\frac{1}{4}$

Now P(head) = $\frac{1}{2}$

But $\frac{1}{2} \times \frac{1}{2} = \frac{1}{4}$ so P(two heads) = P(head) $\times$ P(head)

These results are only true because the events are independent. If they were dependent events, the second probability in the multiplication sum would be different.

> **For independent events P(A and B) = P(A) $\times$ P(B).**

Clearly it is more of a coincidence to throw two heads than one, so it is to be expected that the probability will be less. Multiplying fractions and decimals less than one gives a smaller answer, whereas adding them gives a bigger answer.

STAGE

8

EXAM TIP

It is very common for examination candidates to add probabilities when they should have multiplied. If you get an answer to a probability question that is more than one you have almost certainly added instead of multiplied.

The result for events A and B extends to more than two events. For example in Exercise 3.1, question **2** you should have found that when tossing three coins, the probability of getting all three heads is $\frac{1}{8}$.

$P(\text{head}) \times P(\text{head}) \times P(\text{head}) = \frac{1}{2} \times \frac{1}{2} \times \frac{1}{2} = \frac{1}{8}$

Words that indicate you should use the multiplication rule are 'and', 'both' and 'all'.

EXAMPLE 3

The probability that the school hockey team will win their next match is 0·4.
The probability that they will draw their next match is 0·3.
What is the probability that they will win or draw their next match?

The events are mutually exclusive, since they cannot both win and draw their next match, so:

$P(\text{win or draw}) = P(\text{win}) + P(\text{draw}) = 0.4 + 0.3 = 0.7$

EXAMPLE 4

Matt spins the fair spinner shown in the picture twice.
What is the probability that Matt scores a 4 on both his spins?

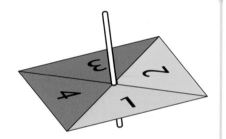

The events are independent, since the second spin cannot be affected by the first.

$P(4 \text{ and } 4) = P(4) \times P(4) = \frac{1}{4} \times \frac{1}{4} = \frac{1}{16}$

EXAMPLE 5

There are six red balls and four black balls in a bag.
Gina selects a ball, notes its colour and replaces it.
She then selects another ball. What is the probability that Gina selects
a) two red balls?   **b)** one of each colour?

Since Gina replaces her first ball before choosing the second the events are independent.

a) $P(\text{two reds}) = P(\text{red}) \times P(\text{red}) = \frac{6}{10} \times \frac{6}{10} = \frac{36}{100} = \frac{9}{25}$ or in decimals $0.6 \times 0.6 = 0.36$

b) Before doing this question it is important to think about what the outcomes are.

Gina requires   first ball red and second ball black
or   first ball black and second ball red.

Both the add and multiply rules are needed.

$P(\text{one of each colour}) = \left(\frac{6}{10} \times \frac{4}{10}\right) + \left(\frac{4}{10} \times \frac{6}{10}\right) = \frac{24}{100} + \frac{24}{100} = \frac{48}{100} = \frac{12}{25}$

or in decimals $(0.6 \times 0.4) + (0.4 \times 0.6) = 0.24 + 0.24 = 0.48$

Questions like part **b)** of Example 5, which require both rules, are clearly more difficult. Later you will see that these can often be more easily tackled using tree diagrams.

EXERCISE 3.2

1 There are five green balls, three red balls and two yellow balls in a bag. If a ball is selected at random, find the probability that it is green or red.

2 The probability that the school hockey team will win their next game is 0·3. The probability that they draw the next game is 0·45. What is the probability that they will win or draw their next game?

3 If the results of the hockey team are independent, use the probability given in question **2** to find the probability they win both their next two games.

4 Craig is choosing his next holiday. The probability that he will choose Ibiza is 0·4, the probability that he will choose Corfu is 0·35 and the probability that he will choose Tenerife is 0·25. Find the probability that Craig chooses Ibiza or Corfu.

5 There are four kings and four queens in a pack of 52 playing cards. Salim chooses a card at random from the pack. What is the probability that it is a king or queen?

6 Janine travels to school by bus, cycle or car. She says that the probability that she travels by bus is 0·25, by cycle is 0·1 and by car is 0·6. Why must she be incorrect?

7 There are five green balls, three red balls and two yellow balls in a bag. Ian chooses a ball at random, notes its colour and puts it back in the bag. He then does this a second time. Find the probability that both Ian's choices are red.

8 Rachel is selecting a main course and a sweet from this menu.

MENU	
Main Course	**Sweet**
Sausage & Chips (0·35)	Apple Pie (0·4)
Ham Salad (0·4)	Fruit Salad (0·6)
Vegetable Lasagne (0·25)	

The numbers next to the items are the probabilities that Rachel chooses those items.

a) Find the probability that Rachel chooses Ham Salad or Vegetable Lasagne for her main course.

b) Assuming her choices are independent, find the probability that Rachel chooses Vegetable Lasagne and Fruit Salad.

9 The probability that I take sandwiches for dinner is 0·4. The probability that I have a school lunch is 0·6. Assuming the events are independent, what is the probability that I have sandwiches on Monday and a school lunch on Tuesday?

10 There are 12 picture cards in a pack of 52 playing cards. John picks a card at random. He then replaces the card and chooses another.

a) Find the probability, as a fraction in its lowest terms, that John's first card is a picture card.

b) Find the probability that both John's cards are picture cards.

11 What is the probability that I get a multiple of 3 when I throw a single fair dice?
    If I throw the dice twice, what is the probability that both throws give a multiple of 3?

12 The weather forecast says 'there is a 40% chance of rain tomorrow'.
    a) Write 40% as a decimal.
    b) Assuming the probability that it rains on any day is independent of whether it rained or not the previous day, find the probability that it rains on two successive days.
    c) State why the assumption made in b) is unlikely to be correct.

13 There are four kings in a pack of 52 playing cards.
    Roger selects a card at random from the pack, returns it to the pack, shuffles the pack and then selects another.
    Find the probability that both Roger's selections were kings.

14 There is an equal likelihood that someone is born on any day of the week. What is the probability that Gary and Rushna were both born on a Monday?

15 The probability that Holly wins the 100-metre race is 0·4.
    The probability that Roberta wins the 400-metre race is 0·3.
    What is the probability that
    a) both girls win their race?
    b) neither of them wins their race?

16 Sally spins this five-sided spinner three times.

What is the probability that all Sally's spins land on 1?

17 Alice and Carol are choosing clothes to go out.
    The probability that Alice chooses jeans is 0·6.
    The probability that Carol chooses jeans is 0·5.
    Assuming that their choices are independent, find the probability that they both choose jeans.
    Explain why this assumption may not be true.

18 Each of the letters of the word INDEPENDENT is written on a card.
    The cards are shuffled and one is selected.
    This card is returned to the pack which is again shuffled.
    A second card is selected.
    What is the probability that the two cards are
    a) both P?
    b) both N?
    c) both a vowel?

19 A box contains a large number of red counters and a large number of black counters.
    25% of the counters are red.
    A counter is chosen from the box, its colour is noted and it is replaced.
    A second counter is then chosen.
    What is the probability that
    a) both counters are red?
    b) both counters are black?
    c) one counter of each colour is chosen?

20 The probability that a darts player hits the bull's eye is 0·6.
    He has three throws at the dart board.
    What is the probability that
    a) he hits the bull's eye each time?
    b) he misses the bull's eye each time?
    c) he hits the bull's eye on two of his three throws?

Using tree diagrams for unequal probabilities

In the first section, tree diagrams were used as a way of organising work on probability when the outcomes were equally likely. It is possible to use them when outcomes are not equally likely.

Look again at Rachel's choices on the menu, from question **8** in Exercise 3.2. These can be shown on a tree diagram with the probabilities written on the branches.

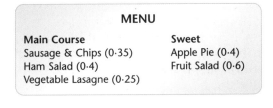

MENU

Main Course	Sweet
Sausage & Chips (0·35)	Apple Pie (0·4)
Ham Salad (0·4)	Fruit Salad (0·6)
Vegetable Lasagne (0·25)	

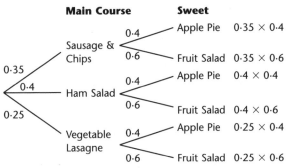

So the probability of choosing Sausage & Chips and Fruit Salad = 0·35 × 0·6 = 0·21 and the probability of choosing Ham Salad and Apple Pie is 0·4 × 0·4 and so on.

If you are going along the 'branches' of a tree diagram, **multiply** the probabilities. At the end, if you want more than one route through the tree, **add** the probabilities.

Now look at Example 5 in a different way.

EXAMPLE 6

There are six red balls and four black balls in a bag.
Gina selects a ball, notes its colour and replaces it. She then selects another ball.
What is the probability that Gina selects
a) two red balls?   **b)** one of each colour?

A tree diagram can be drawn to show this information.

Notice that at each stage the probabilities
add up to 1 and at the end all four
probabilities add up to 1.

1st ball   2nd ball

0·6 — R — 0·6 — R   0·6 × 0·6 = 0·36
           0·4 — B   0·6 × 0·4 = 0·24
0·4 — B — 0·6 — R   0·4 × 0·6 = 0·24
           0·4 — B   0·4 × 0·4 = 0·16

a) Probability of red followed by red
= 0·6 × 0·6 = 0·36.

b) For one of each colour, Gina needs either
the second route or the third route through the tree diagram.
So P(one of each colour) = (0·6 × 0·4) + (0·4 × 0·6) = 0·24 + 0·24 = 0·48.

STAGE
8

1 There are seven red balls and three yellow balls in a bag. Lee chooses a ball at random, notes its colour and replaces it. He then chooses another.
Copy and complete the tree diagram to show Lee's choices.

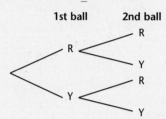

What is the probability that Lee chooses
a) two red balls?
b) a red ball and then a yellow ball?
c) a yellow ball and then a red ball?
d) a red ball and a yellow ball in either order?

2 On any day the probability that Sarah's bus is late is 0·2.
Copy the tree diagram and complete it for two days.

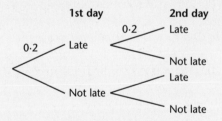

Calculate the probability that Sarah's bus is
a) late on both days.
b) late on one of the two days.

3 Li is choosing a starter and main course from this menu. The probabilities of each of her choices are in brackets next to the items.

MENU
Starter
Soup (0·3)
Spring Rolls (0·7)
Main Course
Chicken Fried Rice (0·3)
Beef Satay (0·2)
Sweet & Sour Pork (0·5)

a) Draw a tree diagram to show Li's choices.
b) Calculate the probability that Li chooses
  (i) Spring Rolls and Beef Satay.
  (ii) Soup and Sweet & Sour Pork.

4 The probability that Andy wakes up when his alarm goes off is 0·8.
Copy the tree diagram and complete it for the first two days of the week.

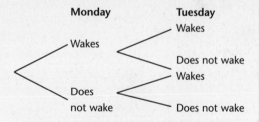

Calculate the probability that Andy
a) wakes on both days.
b) wakes on one of the two days.

Probability

3

STAGE
8

5 In an experiment a drawing pin falls point up 300 times in 500 throws.

a) Write down, as a fraction in its lowest terms, the probability of the pin landing point up.

b) Draw a tree diagram to show the result of two throws, and the pin landing point up or point down.

c) Find the probability that the pin lands point up on

(i) both throws.

(ii) one of the two throws.

6 Extend the tree diagram you drew for question **5** to show the results of three throws.
Find the probability that the pin lands point up on

a) all three throws.

b) one of the three throws.

7 There are five red balls, two blue balls and three yellow balls in a bag.
Susan chooses a ball at random, notes its colour and replaces it.
She then chooses another.

a) Draw a tree diagram to show the results of Susan's choices.

b) Calculate the probability that Susan chooses

(i) two red balls.

(ii) two balls of the same colour.

8 There are ten red balls, three blue balls and seven yellow balls in a bag.
Waseem chooses a ball at random, notes its colour and replaces it.
He then chooses another.

a) Draw a tree diagram to show the results of Waseem's choices.

b) Calculate the probability that Waseem chooses

(i) two blue balls.

(ii) two balls of the same colour.

(iii) two balls of different colours. (Look for the quick way of doing it.)

9 Brian drew this tree diagram for the results of choosing coloured balls from a bag.

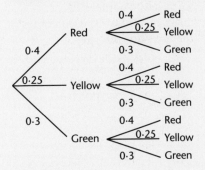

Explain why Brian must have made a mistake.

10 Terry is playing a board game where two dice are thrown each turn.
To start the game he must throw the two dice and get two sixes.

a) Copy and complete the tree diagram.

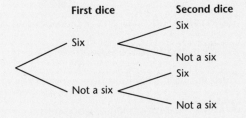

b) Use the tree diagram to work out the probability that

(i) Terry gets two sixes.

(ii) Terry gets just one six.

EXERCISE 3.3 continued

11 The probability that the school team win, draw or lose any match is 0·5, 0·3 and 0·2 respectively.

a) Copy and complete the tree diagram to show the outcomes of the next two matches.

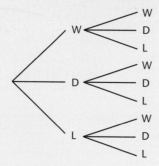

First match   Second match

b) Work out the probability that

(i) the team win both of their matches.

(ii) the team win one of the two matches.

(iii) the results of the two matches are the same.

C CHALLENGE 1

There are *x* red balls and *y* blue balls in a bag.

A ball is chosen at random from the bag.

Then the ball is replaced and another is chosen.

What is the probability of choosing

a) one ball of each colour?

b) two balls of the same colour?

Give your answers in terms of *x* and *y* as a single fraction in its simplest form.

KEY IDEAS

- Tree diagrams can be used to show possible outcomes of two or more events and their probabilities. When going along the branches of a tree diagram, multiply the probabilities. If more than one route is wanted, add the probabilities.

- If events are mutually exclusive then P(A or B) = P(A) + P(B).

- For independent events P(A and B) = P(A) × P(B).

4 Equations and inequalities

You will learn about

- Solving equations involving brackets
- Solving equations involving fractions
- Solving harder inequalities

You should already know

- How to write a formula using letters
- How to collect together algebraic expressions
- How to expand brackets
- How to form and solve simple linear equations
- How to form and solve simple inequalities

Solving equations with fractions

You may have to solve equations involving fractions.

STAGE

8

EXAMPLE 1

Solve the equation $\frac{x}{3} = 2x - 3$.

$$\frac{x}{3} = 2x - 3$$

$x = 3(2x - 3)$ Multiply both sides by 3.

$x = 6x - 9$ Multiply out the bracket.

$x + 9 = 6x$ Add 9 to both sides.

$9 = 6x - x$ Subtract x from both sides.
This moves the x-terms on to the right-hand side of the equation so the final x-term will be positive.

$9 = 5x$

$x = \frac{9}{5}$ or $1\frac{4}{5}$ or $1 \cdot 8$ Divide both sides by 5.

EXAM TIP

A common error when multiplying through by a number or letter is to multiply just the first term. Use brackets to make sure.

Another common error in examples like these would be to give the answer as $\frac{5}{9}$ rather than $\frac{9}{5}$.

It is much easier to move all the x-terms on to the side where the final x-term will be positive.

EXAMPLE 2

Solve the equation $\dfrac{400}{x} = 8$.

$$\dfrac{400}{x} = 8$$

$400 = 8x$ Multiply both sides by x.

$x = 50$ Divide both sides by 8.

EXAMPLE 3

Solve $\frac{1}{2}(3x + 2) = 10$.

> Note that this equation could be written $\dfrac{3x + 2}{2} = 10$. The solution would be identical.

$2 \times \frac{1}{2}(3x + 2) = 10 \times 2$ Multiply both sides by 2. You may be able to miss this line out and go straight to the next.

$3x + 2 = 20$ Because $2 \times \frac{1}{2} = 1$.

$3x = 18$ Subtract 2 from both sides.

$x = 6$ Divide both sides by 3.

Notice that it is much easier to multiply both sides of the equation by a number that will eliminate fractions than to multiply brackets out.

EXAMPLE 4

Solve $\dfrac{x}{3} + \dfrac{x}{2} = 5$.

$$\dfrac{x}{3} + \dfrac{x}{2} = 5$$

$\dfrac{x}{3} \times 6 + \dfrac{x}{2} \times 6 = 5 \times 6$ Multiply every term by 6 because 6 is the common denominator of $\dfrac{x}{3}$ and $\dfrac{x}{2}$. This will eliminate both fractions.

$2x + 3x = 30$

$5x = 30$

$x = 6$ Divide both sides by 5.

STAGE

8

Equations involving brackets

You have already learnt how to solve equations with a pair of brackets on both sides. The following examples show you how to solve equations where there are more than one pair of brackets on one side.

EXAMPLE 5

Solve $4(2x - 3) + 2(x + 3) = 29$.

$8x - 12 + 2x + 6 = 29$ Multiply out the brackets.
$[8x + 2x - 12 + 6 = 29]$
$10x - 6 = 29$ Collect the like terms on the left-hand side.
$[10x - 6 + 6 = 29 + 6]$ Add 6 to each side.
$10x = 35$
$x = 3 \cdot 5$ Divide by 10.

You may feel that you can miss out the lines in square brackets.

EXAMPLE 6

Solve $2(x - 3) - 5(x + 4) = {}^-20$.

$2x - 6 - 5x - 20 = {}^-20$ Multiply out the brackets, notice that $({}^-5) \times ({}^+4) = {}^-20$.
$[2x - 5x - 6 - 20 = {}^-20]$
${}^-3x - 26 = {}^-20$ Collect the like terms on the left-hand side.
${}^-26 = {}^-20 + 3x$ Add 3x to each side so that the x-term is positive.
$[{}^-26 + 20 = 3x]$ Add 20 to each side.
${}^-6 = 3x$
$x = {}^-2$ Divide by 3.

EXERCISE 4.1

Solve these equations.

1   $\frac{x}{2} = 3x - 10$

2   $\frac{x}{3} = x - 4$

3   $\frac{2x}{3} = x - 2$

4   $\frac{2x}{5} = x - 3$

5   $\frac{3x}{2} = 7 - 2x$

6   $\frac{3x}{5} = 4 - x$

7   $\frac{5x}{3} = 4x - 2$

8   $\frac{2x}{3} = 4x - 5$

EXERCISE 4.1 continued

9 $\frac{x}{3} + 5 = 9$

10 $\frac{2x}{7} - 2 = 5$

11 $\frac{50}{x} = 2$

12 $\frac{300}{x} = 15$

13 $\frac{200}{x} = 4$

14 $\frac{25}{2x} = 5$

15 $\frac{39}{2x} = 3$

16 $\frac{1}{3}(x - 2) = 7$

17 $\frac{1}{4}(2x - 3) = 1$

18 $\frac{3x - 1}{5} = 4$

19 $\frac{5x - 12}{2} = x$

20 $\frac{3}{4}(x - 3) = 6$

21 $\frac{5}{x} + 3 = 7$

22 $\frac{6}{x} - 5 = {}^-1$

23 $\frac{7}{2x} - 2 = 3$

24 $\frac{5}{3x} + 7 = 10$

25 $\frac{x}{2} - \frac{x}{4} = 3$

26 $\frac{2x}{5} + \frac{x}{3} = 22$

27 $\frac{3x}{2} - \frac{x}{6} = 12$

28 $\frac{x}{2} - 4 = \frac{x}{3}$

29 $3(x - 7) + 4x = 5(x - 4)$

30 $5(x - 2) - 3x = 2(5 - x)$

31 $2(x + 4) + 3(x - 1) = 30$

32 $5(x - 3) + 3(x - 2) = 15$

33 $3(2x + 7) + 2(x - 2) = 1$

34 $4(x - 3) - 2(x + 1) = 10$

35 $5(3x + 4) - 10(x - 2) = 60$

36 $3(2x + 1) + 2(2x - 7) = 30$

37 $4(2x - 7) - 2(x - 8) = 3$

38 $4(x + 1) + 3(x - 2) - 5(x - 2) = 2$

C CHALLENGE 1

Solve these equations.

a) $\frac{x + 2}{3} + \frac{x - 3}{2} = 5$

Hint: Multiply every term by 6.

b) $\frac{x - 2}{4} - \frac{x + 3}{5} = 1$

STAGE
8

Solving inequalities

As with equations, you may get inequalities containing fractions or brackets.

The method of solving inequalities is similar to the method of solving equations. The one difference is that when you move the x-terms on to one side of the equation, the final x-term must be positive.

This is illustrated in the following examples.

EXAMPLE 7

Solve $\dfrac{x}{3} \geqslant 2x - 3$ and show your answer on a number line.

$$\dfrac{x}{3} \geqslant 2x - 3$$

$x \geqslant 3(2x - 3)$ Multiply both sides by 3.

$x \geqslant 6x - 9$ Multiply out the brackets. You may be able to go straight to this line.

$x + 9 \geqslant 6x$ Add 9 to both sides.

$9 \geqslant 5x$ Subtract x from both sides. Notice we have moved the x-terms to the right-hand side so that the x-term will be positive.

$\dfrac{9}{5} \geqslant x$ Divide both sides by 5.

$x \leqslant \dfrac{9}{5}$ or $x \leqslant 1\frac{4}{5}$ or $x \leqslant 1 \cdot 8$ Change the inequality to make x the subject. Notice that this means the inequality changes round.

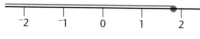

EXAM TIP

Remember the solution of an inequality is itself an inequality. A common mistake in a question like Example 7 is to simply write $1\frac{4}{5}$ or $1 \cdot 8$ in the answer space.

EXAMPLE 8

Solve $\dfrac{5 - 2x}{3} \leqslant 7$.

$$\dfrac{5 - 2x}{3} \leqslant 7$$

$5 - 2x \leqslant 21$ Multiply both sides by 3.

$5 \leqslant 21 + 2x$ Add $2x$ to both sides. Notice we move the x-term to the right-hand side so that it will be positive.

$^{-}16 \leqslant 2x$ Subtract 21 from both sides. Remember $5 - 21 = {^{-}16}$.

$^{-}8 \leqslant x$ Divide both sides by 2.

$x \geqslant {^{-}8}$ Make x the subject.

EXAMPLE 9

Solve $\frac{1}{2}(6x - 3) < 2x + 5$.

$\frac{1}{2}(6x - 3) < 2x + 5$

$6x - 3 < 4x + 10$ Multiply both sides by 2.

$6x < 4x + 13$ Add 3 to both sides.

$2x < 13$ Subtract 4x from both sides. Notice that this time the x-term will be positive if we move the x-terms to the left-hand side.

$x < 6\frac{1}{2}$ Divide both sides by 2.

EXAM TIP

Always move the x-terms on to the side where the result will be positive.

This is because the rules change if you multiply or divide by a negative number.

When you multiply or divide an inequality by a negative number, you must change $<$ to $>$, and $>$ to $<$. Moving the terms on to the side where the result will be positive gets round this problem.

EXERCISE 4.2

Solve these inequalities.

1   $\frac{x}{3} \geqslant 5$

2   $\frac{3x}{2} < 4$

3   $\frac{x}{4} \geqslant x - 6$

4   $\frac{x}{3} \geqslant 3x - 12$

5   $12(x - 4) \leqslant 3(2x - 6)$

6   $\frac{2x}{3} < 3x - 14$

7   $5(2x - 1) > 4(3x - 2)$

8   $\frac{1}{2}(2 - x) < 9$

9   $\frac{2x - 3}{3} \leqslant 5$

10   $\frac{x}{2} \geqslant \frac{3x}{4} - 2$

11   $7 - \frac{x}{3} \geqslant 3$

12   $\frac{3x}{2} > \frac{x}{4} + 2$

13   $\frac{1}{4}(2x + 1) \leqslant 8$

14   $\frac{1}{5}(3x + 2) \geqslant 7$

15   $\frac{2(x + 3)}{3} < 8$

16   $\frac{1}{2}(5 - 2x) > 6$

17   $\frac{1}{3}(2x + 1) \leqslant 4x$

18   $\frac{1}{4}(2x + 1) \leqslant 2x - 2$

19   $\frac{2}{3}(2x + 1) \geqslant 2x - 6$

20   $5(x - 1) > \frac{1}{2}(3x + 4)$

STAGE

8

C CHALLENGE 2

Solve the inequality $x^2 < 36$.

Forming equations and inequalities

Some problems can be solved using equations and inequalities.

EXAMPLE 10

The angles of a triangle are as shown in the diagram.

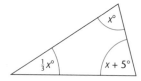

a) Write down an equation in x.

b) Solve the equation to find the angles of the triangle.

a) Since the total angle of a triangle is 180°

$x + \frac{1}{3}x + x + 5 = 180$

$2\frac{1}{3}x = 175$ Subtract 5 from both sides.

b) $2\frac{1}{3}x = 175$

$7x = 525$ Multiply both terms by 3.

$x = 75$ Divide both sides by 7.

The three angles of the triangle are 75°, 25° and 80°.

STAGE

8

EXAMPLE 11

Jane's age is one-third of her father's.
In 15 years' time her age will be more than half of her father's.

Let her father's age be x years.

a) Write down expressions in terms of x for each of these.
   (i) Jane's age now
   (ii) Jane's age in 15 years' time
   (iii) Her father's age in 15 years' time

b) Write down an inequality in x.

c) Solve the inequality to find the greatest age Jane's father can be.

a) (i) $\frac{1}{3}x$　　　　**(ii)** $\frac{1}{3}x + 15$　　　　**(iii)** $x + 15$

b) $\frac{1}{3}x + 15 > \frac{1}{2}(x + 15)$

c) $2x + 90 > 3(x + 15)$　　　Multiply every term by 6 to eliminate both fractions.

$2x + 90 > 3x + 45$　　　Multiply out the brackets.

$90 > x + 45$　　　Subtract $2x$ from both sides. This means that the x is positive on the right-hand side.

$45 > x$　　　Take 45 from both sides.

$x < 45$　　　Make x the subject.

This means that the greatest age Jane's father can be is 44 years.

EXERCISE 4.3

1 A triangle has a base of b cm and a height of 5 cm. The area is 30 cm². Write down an equation in b and solve it to find the length of the base.

2 Maisey thinks of a number. Her number divided by three gives the same number as taking the number away from sixteen. Let the number be n.
Write down an equation in n and solve it to find the number Maisey thought of.

3 A greengrocer sold potatoes at x pence per kilogram. He paid $\frac{2}{3}$ what he sold them for.
His profit per kilogram was 20p.
a) Write down an equation in x.
b) Solve the equation to find how much he sold the potatoes for.

4 The lengths of the sides in this triangle are in centimetres.

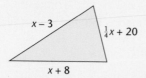

The perimeter of this triangle is 106 cm.
a) Write down an equation in x.
b) Solve the equation to find the lengths of the sides in this triangle.

5 Ahmed had £x.
He spent £4 on books and still had three-fifths of his money left.
a) Write down an equation in x.
b) Solve your equation to find out how much money Ahmed started with.

6 Ayesha earns £x. Ben earns two-thirds as much as Ayesha. They need at least £60 to go to a concert.
a) Write down an inequality in x.
b) Solve the inequality to find how much Ayesha must earn for them to go to the concert.

7 Jess had £20. She spent £x.
The amount she has left is less than one-quarter of what she has spent.
a) Write down an inequality in x.
b) Solve the inequality to find the smallest amount Jess could have spent.

8 A roll of cloth had 100 metres on it. A customer bought x metres. Another customer bought one-quarter of what was left.
The maximum amount left on the roll is 40 metres.
a) Write down an inequality in x.
b) Solve the inequality to find the smallest amount the first customer could have bought.

9 Graham is half as old as his father. Eighteen years ago he was less than one-fifth as old as his father.
Let his father's age be x.
a) Write down expressions in terms of x for each of these.
   (i) Graham's age now
   (ii) Graham's age 18 years ago
   (iii) His father's age 18 years ago
b) Write down an inequality in x.
c) Solve the inequality to find the maximum age Graham's father could be now.

10 The angles of a quadrilateral are as shown in the diagram.

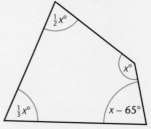

a) Write down an equation in x.
b) Solve the equation to find the angles of the quadrilateral.

K KEY IDEAS

- To solve equations involving fractions, first multiply every term in the equation by the lowest common multiple of the denominators, expand any brackets and then rearrange as usual.

- Linear inequalities are solved using the same rules as equations, except that it is important that you move the x-terms on to the side which will make the resulting x-term positive.

Revision exercise A1

1 Work out these.

   a) $1\frac{2}{5} + 3\frac{1}{4}$

   b) $2\frac{5}{6} + 1\frac{7}{8}$

   c) $4\frac{7}{10} - 1\frac{2}{5}$

   d) $3\frac{1}{4} - 2\frac{2}{3}$

   e) $\frac{2}{3} + 4\frac{1}{2} - 2\frac{5}{6}$

   f) $2\frac{4}{7} \times 1\frac{5}{6}$

   g) $2\frac{1}{2} \times 3\frac{1}{5}$

   h) $6 \div 2\frac{2}{3}$

2 To make a frame, John uses four pieces of wood: two are $4\frac{1}{4}$ inches long and two are $6\frac{2}{3}$ inches long.
   He cut them all off a piece of wood 24 inches long.
   How much wood was left?

3 a) Draw the graph of $y = x^3 - 7x$ for values of x from $^-3$ to 3.
   b) Use your graph to solve the equation $x^3 - 7x = 0$.

4 Sketch the graphs of these curves.
   a) $y = x^3$
   b) $y = \frac{12}{x}$

5 Here are four equations.

   a) $y = 2x^2$

   b) $y = 2x + 1$

   c) $y = {}^{-}2x^3$

   d) $y = \frac{2}{x}$

   The graphs of these equations are sketched here. They are not in the correct order. Match each graph with the correct equation.

   (i)
   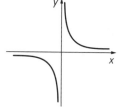

   (ii)
   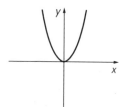

   (iii)
   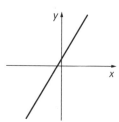

   (iv)
   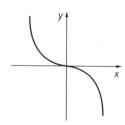

6 Each of the letters of the word STATISTICS is written on a card.
The cards are shuffled and a card is drawn at random.
The card is then replaced, the cards reshuffled and another card is drawn at random.
Calculate the probability that the letter on both cards is
a) A.
b) I.
c) S.

7 The probability that the school bus is late on a Monday is 0·3.
The probability that it is late on a Tuesday is 0·2.
Assuming these probabilities are independent, find the probability that the bus is late on
a) both days.
b) neither day.

8 Mr and Mrs Brown intend to have three children.
Draw a tree diagram for the possible sexes of the three children.
Assuming that for each child they are equally likely to have a boy or a girl, find the probability that
a) all three children are girls.
b) Mr and Mrs Brown have two boys and a girl.

9 The whole of Year 9 takes tests in English, Maths and Science.
The probability that a randomly chosen student passes English is 0·8, Maths is 0·7 and Science is 0·9.
Copy and complete the tree diagram for the three subjects.

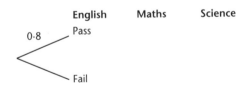

Calculate the probability that a randomly chosen Year 9 student
a) passes all three subjects.
b) passes two out of the three subjects.

10 Solve these equations.

a) $\frac{x}{2} = 3x - 10$

b) $\frac{x}{3} = 3 - 2x$

c) $\frac{500}{x} = 20$

d) $\frac{300}{x} = 60$

e) $\frac{3x}{4} + \frac{x}{12} = 60$

f) $\frac{x-1}{7} = 3$

g) $\frac{1}{5}(4x - 9) = 7$

h) $\frac{4x}{3} + 2x = 20$

i) $4(x + 2) + 2(3x - 1) = 56$

j) $5(x - 2) - 3(x + 1) = 2$

11 Solve these inequalities.

a) $\frac{x}{3} \geqslant x - 12$

b) $\frac{x}{5} \geqslant 2x - 9$

c) $3(2x - 3) > 5(2x - 5)$

d) $\frac{2x}{3} > \frac{x}{6} + 5$

e) $\frac{2x-1}{4} \leqslant 7$

f) $\frac{1}{2}(3x - 14) \leqslant 5x$

g) $4(x - 1) > \frac{1}{3}(2x + 5)$

12 The lengths of the sides in this triangle are in centimetres.

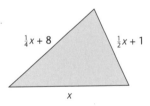

The perimeter of this triangle is 30 cm.
a) Write down an equation in x.
b) Solve the equation to find the lengths of the sides in this triangle.

13 Abigail has £100. She spends £x on a pair of jeans and then two-thirds of what she has left on a pair of trainers.

a) Write down, in terms of x, expressions for each of these.

    (i) How much she had left after she bought the jeans

    (ii) How much she spent on the trainers

    (iii) How much she spent in total on the jeans and trainers

b) Abigail sees a top for £20. Write down an inequality that states that she has enough money left to buy the top.

c) Solve the inequality to find the most Abigail could have paid for the jeans if she is able to buy the top.

Percentage increase and decrease

5

You will learn about

- Finding percentage increases and decreases using a multiplier
- Calculating the original amount when given the final amount after a percentage increase or decrease

You should already know

- Fraction, decimal and percentage notation
- Multiplication and division of decimals by 100
- How to calculate a percentage of a given quantity
- How to increase and decrease a quantity by a given percentage (This will be looked at again in this chapter.)
- How to calculate simple interest
- How to round an amount of money to the nearest penny.

Percentage increase

You have already met two ways of increasing a quantity by a percentage. You can either calculate the percentage increase and add it on or, more efficiently, you can calculate the percentage increase and add it on in one step by using a multiplier. Example 1 shows the method of using a multiplier.

STAGE
8

5

EXAMPLE 1

Increase £24 000 by 3%.

You need to calculate 3% of £24 000 and add it on to the original £24 000.

You need 3% of 24 000 + 100% of 24 000.

This is the same as 103% of £24 000.

The calculation now becomes

$£24\,000 \times \frac{103}{100} = £24\,000 \times 1\cdot03$

$= £24\,720.$

Using this method, you carry out the percentage calculation and the addition in one step.

Percentage decrease

In the same way, to reduce a quantity by a percentage, you can either calculate the percentage decrease and take it off or you can calculate the percentage decrease and take it off in one step by using a multiplier. Example 2 shows the method of using a multiplier.

EXAMPLE 2

Reduce £17·60 by 15%.

You need to find 15% of £17·60 and subtract the answer from £17·60.

You need 100% of £17·60 – 15% of £17·60.

This is the same as 85% of £17·60 (since 100% – 15% = 85%).

The calculation now becomes

$£17\cdot60 \times \frac{85}{100} = £17\cdot60 \times 0\cdot85$

$= £14\cdot96.$

Using this method, you carry out the percentage calculation and the subtraction in one step.

EXERCISE 5.1

1 What do you multiply a quantity by if it is increased by each of these?
a) 6%
b) 9%
c) 17·5%
d) 1·25%
e) 4%
f) 18%
g) 12·5%
h) 5·6%

2 What do you multiply a quantity by if it is decreased by each of these?
a) 6%
b) 9%
c) 17·5%
d) 1·25%

3 Increase £400 by each of these.
a) 5%
b) 20%
c) 80%

4 Increase £4800 by each of these.
a) 5%
b) 23%
c) 79%

5 Decrease £200 by each of these.
a) 4%
b) 30%
c) 70%

6 Decrease £760 by each of these.
a) 8%
b) 17%
c) 63%

7 Saira's electricity bill is £160 before VAT is added on.
What is the bill after VAT at 5% is added on?

8 A factory employs 1350 people.
The management decides to make cutbacks which will reduce the number of employees by 18%.
How many employees will be left?

9 The area of a sports field is 80 000 m². 15% of the field is sold for housing. How much is left?

10 A piece of elastic is stretched by 17%. If it was originally 90 cm long, what is its new length?

11 Train fares went up by 7%.
What is the new price of a ticket which previously cost £4?

12 Colin pays 6% of his pay into a pension fund.
If he earns £840 per month, what will his pay be after taking off his pension payments?

13 In a sale all items are reduced by 20%. What is the sale price of an article which originally cost £24?

14 A computer costs £690 before VAT is added on.
What will it cost after VAT is added on at 17·5%?

15 Samina earns £4 per hour.
What will she earn if she receives a wage increase of 3%?

16 A firm claims that its insulation will cut heating bills by 25%.
Mr and Mrs Brown's annual heating bill is £830 at the moment. What will the bill be if the firm's claim is justified?

17 Mike earns £150 per week.
He pays 6% of this into a pension fund. How much money is he left with?

18 The price of petrol went up by 120% in the period from 1990 to 2000.
If it was 36p per litre in 1990, what was it in 2000?

CHALLENGE 1

House prices rose by 12% in 2003, 11% in 2004 and 7% in 2005.

At the start of 2003 the price of a house was £120000.

What was the price at the end of 2005? Give your answer to the nearest pound.

Express the price at the end of 2005 as a percentage of the price at the start of 2003.

CHALLENGE 2

The value of an investment rose by 8% in 2004 and fell by 8% in 2005.

If the value of the investment was £3000 at the start of 2004, what was the value at the end of 2005? Express the final increase or decrease as a percentage of the original investment.

Finding the original quantity

If a quantity is increased by 20%, then you have just found that

new amount = original amount × 1·2

It follows that

original amount = new amount ÷ 1·2

EXAMPLE 3

Bert received an increase of 20% in his salary.
After the increase he was earning £31 260.
What was his salary before the rise?

new salary = old salary × 1·2

old salary = new salary ÷ 1·2
= £31 260 ÷ 1·2
= £26 050

If a quantity is decreased by 10%, then you have just found that

new amount = original amount × 0·9.

It follows that

original amount = new amount ÷ 0·9

EXAMPLE 4

Irene paid £38·70 for a skirt in a sale.
This was after it had been reduced by 10%.
What was the original price of the skirt?

new price = original price × 0·9

original price = new price ÷ 0·9
$$= £38·70 ÷ 0·9$$
$$= £43$$

EXERCISE 5.2

In this exercise, some of the questions ask for the original amount and some ask for the new amount.

1 A price of £50 is increased by 7·5%.
What is the new price?

2 After an increase of 12%, a quantity is 84 tonnes.
What was it before the increase?

3 A quantity is decreased by 3%.
It is now 38·8.
What was it to start with?

4 In a sale everything is reduced by 5%.
A pair of shoes costs £47·50 in the sale.
How much did they cost before the sale?

5 A coat was advertised at £79.
In a sale the price was reduced by 5%.
What was the new price?

6 A newspaper increased its circulation by 3% and the new number sold was 58 195.
What was it before the increase?

7 Mr Dale made a profit of £13 250 in the year 2000.
This was an increase of 6% on his profit in 1999.
What was his profit in 1999?

8 Santos sold his car for £8520. This was 40% less than he paid for it five years before.
What did he pay for it?

9 In a local election in 1997, Labour received 1375 votes.
This was increased by 12% in 1998.
How many people voted Labour in 1998?

10 A charity's income has been reduced by $2\frac{1}{2}$%.
Its income is now £8580.
What was it before the reduction?

11 Stephen was given a rise of 7%.
His salary after the rise was £28 890.
What was it before the rise?

STAGE 8

EXERCISE 5.2 continued

12 It was announced that the number of people unemployed had decreased by 3%.
The number who were unemployed before the decrease was 2·56 million. How many are now unemployed?
Give the answer to three significant figures.

13 Between 1978 and 1979 house prices increased by 12·5%.
A house was valued at £27 000 in 1979. What was its value in 1978?

14 The cost of a car, including VAT at 17·5%, is £12 925.
What is the cost without VAT?

15 A holiday cost £564, including VAT at 17·5%.
What was the cost without VAT?

16 At Percival's sale the price of everything is reduced by $7\frac{1}{2}$%, rounded to the nearest penny.
a) A pair of boots cost £94·99 before the sale.
What is the price in the sale?
b) Delia is charged £13·87 for a blouse in the sale.
What was its original price?

17 At Jack's café all prices were increased by 5% (to the nearest penny).
a) A cup of tea cost 75p before the increase.
What is the new price?
b) The new price of a cup of coffee is £1·30.
What did it cost before the increase?

C CHALLENGE 3

a) A jumper was reduced by 12·5% in a sale. The reduction was £7·50.
What was the sale price?

b) There are 36 more girls than boys in a school. 54% of the students at the school are girls. How many girls are there at the school?

K KEY IDEAS

- To increase a quantity by, for example 5%, a quick way is to multiply by 1·05.

- To reduce a quantity by, for example 12%, a quick way is to multiply by 0·88 (as 100 − 12 = 88).

- If an amount has been increased by, for example 5% and you know the new amount, you find the original by dividing by 1·05.

- If an amount has been reduced by, for example 12% and you know the new amount, you find the original by dividing by 0·88.

Linear inequalities

6

A   ACTIVITY 1

a) Draw a set of axes with both x and y taking values from $^-6$ to 6.
Draw the line $y = 3$ on the grid.
Shade the region above the line.

What can you say about all the points in the region you have shaded?
Try to write this as an inequality.

What about points on the line? Are they included?

b) Draw a set of axes with both x and y taking values from $^-6$ to 6.
Draw the line $y = x + 1$ on the grid.
Shade the region underneath the line.

What can you say about all the points in the region you have shaded?
Try to write this as an inequality.

What about points on the line? Are they included?

STAGE
8

In Activity 1, you did not distinguish between the inequalities $y > 3$ and $y \geqslant 3$. There is a convention you can use if you wish to distinguish between them.

When an inequality involves the signs $<$ or $>$, the points on the line are *not* included in the solution.

For example, if $x < 2$, the points on the line $x = 2$, for example $(2, {}^-2)$, $(2, {}^-1)$, $(2, 0)$, $(2, 1)$, $(2, 2)$ and so on, do not satisfy the inequality.

An inequality involving the signs $<$ or $>$ is represented on a graph using a dashed line.

An inequality involving the signs $\leqslant$ or $\geqslant$ is represented by an unbroken line.

Showing regions on graphs

It is often possible to show the region on a graph that satisfies an inequality.

EXAMPLE 1

Write down the inequality that describes the region shaded in each graph.

a)

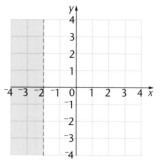

b)

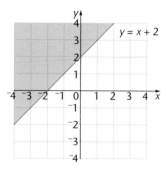

a) $x < {}^-2$

The line drawn is $x = {}^-2$.
This line divides the graph into two regions $x < {}^-2$ and $x > {}^-2$.
The shaded region is $x < {}^-2$.
Check by testing any point in the region.

b) $y \geqslant x + 2$

The line is $y = x + 2$ and divides the graph into two regions $y < x + 2$ and $y > x + 2$.
To decide which side is shaded choose any point not on the line and test it, for example $(0, 0)$.
Here $x + 2 = 2$, and $y = 0$, so $y < x + 2$ at $(0, 0)$ and $(0, 0)$ is not in the region.
Since the line $y = x + 2$ is an unbroken line, points on the line are included.
The shaded region is $y \geqslant x + 2$.

EXAMPLE 2

On separate grids shade each of theses regions.

a) $y \geqslant 2$

b) $y < 2x - 3$

a) It is clear that $y > 2$ is above the line $y = 2$.
$y = 2$ is included, so draw an unbroken line.

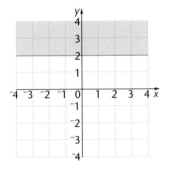

b) Draw the line $y = 2x - 3$.
Since $y = 2x - 3$ is not included, draw a dashed line.
Then the two regions are $y > 2x - 3$ and $y < 2x - 3$.
To test which side is wanted, choose any point not on the line, for example $(0, 0)$.
Here $y = 0$ and $2x - 3 = {}^-3$,
so $y > 2x - 3$ at $(0, 0)$.
Therefore $(0, 0)$ is not in the region required.
Shade the other region.

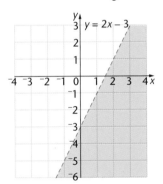

EXAM TIP

When testing a region, if possible use $(0, 0)$. If the line goes through $(0, 0)$ choose a point with positive coordinates, for example $(1, 0)$, to test the region.

STAGE

8

EXERCISE 6.1

For questions **1** to **8**, write down the inequality that describes the shaded region.

1

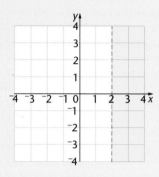

2

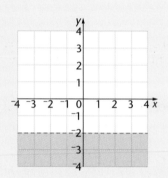

3

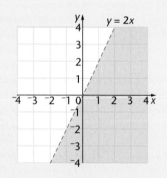

$y = 2x$

4

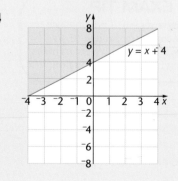

$y = x + 4$

5

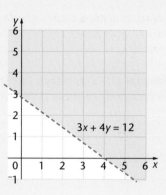

$3x + 4y = 12$

6

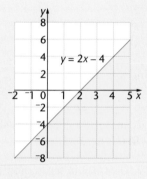

$y = 2x - 4$

7

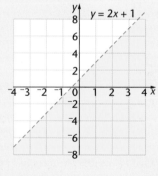

$y = 2x + 1$

8

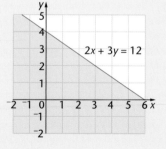

$2x + 3y = 12$

EXERCISE 6.1 continued

9 Draw a set of axes and label them from ⁻4 to 4 for x and y.
Shade the region $y > $ ⁻3.

10 Draw a set of axes and label them from ⁻4 to 4 for x and y.
Shade the region $x \geqslant $ ⁻1.

11 Draw a set of axes. Label them from ⁻3 to 6 for x and from ⁻3 to 5 for y.
Shade the region $2x + 5y < 10$.

12 Draw a set of axes. Label them from ⁻1 to 6 for x and from ⁻2 to 5 for y.
Shade the region $4x + 5y \leqslant 20$.

13 Draw a set of axes and label them from 0 to 5 for x and y.
Shade the region $3x + 5y > 15$.

Representing regions satisfying more than one inequality

When you wish to represent a region that satisfies more than one inequality, it is often better to shade the region that *does not* satisfy the inequality; the region that *does* satisfy the inequality is left unshaded.

Several inequalities can be represented on the same axes and the region where the values of x and y satisfy all of them may be found.

EXAMPLE 3

Draw a set of axes and label them 0 to 8 for both x and y.
Show, by shading, the region where $x \geqslant 0$, $y \geqslant 0$ and $x + 2y \leqslant 8$.

First draw the line $x + 2y = 8$.

Then shade the regions $x < 0$, $y < 0$ and $x + 2y > 8$. These are the regions which are *not required* for the solution; that is, where the values of x and y *do not* satisfy the inequalities.

The required region, where the values of x and y satisfy all three inequalities, is left unshaded. It is labelled R.

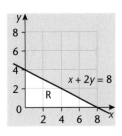

STAGE

8

EXAMPLE 4

Draw a set of axes and label them from 0 to 5 for both x and y.
Show, by shading, the region where $x \geqslant 0$, $y \geqslant 0$, $5x + 4y < 20$ and $2x + y > 4$.

Draw the two lines $5x + 4y = 20$ and $2x + y = 4$.
Because they represent the inequalities $5x + 4y < 20$
and $2x + y > 4$ the lines should be dashed, not
unbroken. Label them clearly.

Shade the regions $x < 0$, $y < 0$, $5x + 4y > 20$ and
$2x + y < 4$.

The required region is labelled R.

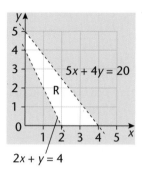

EXERCISE 6.2

1 Draw a set of axes and label them
0 to 6 for both x and y.
Show, by shading, the region where
$x \geqslant 0$, $y \geqslant 0$ and $x + 2y \leqslant 6$.

2 Draw a set of axes and label them from
0 to 12 for x and from 0 to 8 for y.
Show by shading the region where
$y > 0$, $x > 0$ and $3x + 5y < 30$.

3 Draw a set of axes. Label them $^-1$ to 4
for x and from $^-3$ to 4 for y.
Show, by shading, the region where
$x \geqslant 0$, $y \leqslant 3$ and $y \geqslant 2x - 3$.

4 Draw a set of axes and label them
$^-4$ to 4 for both x and y.
Show, by shading, the region where
$x > ^-2$, $y < 3$ and $y > 2x$.

5 Draw a set of axes and label them
0 to 6 for both x and y.
Show, by shading, the region where
$x < 4$, $y < 3$ and $3x + 4y \leqslant 12$.

6 Draw a set of axes and label them
$^-1$ to 5 for both x and y.
Show, by shading, the region where
$y \geqslant 0$, $y \leqslant x + 1$ and $3x + 5y < 15$.

7 Draw a set of axes and label them from
$^-1$ to 8 for x and from $^-1$ to 7 for y.
Show by shading the region where
$x > 0$, $3x + 8y > 24$ and $5x + 4y < 20$.

STAGE
8

CHALLENGE 1

At James and Nicola's wedding, 56 people need to be taken to the reception.

Harry's Hire Cars has nine four-seater cars costing £25 each and five eight-seater cars costing £35 each.

James and Nicola hire x four-seater and y eight-seater cars.

a) One inequality is $x \leqslant 9$.
Write down two other inequalities that must be satisfied.

b) Draw these three inequalities on a graph and shade the regions not required.

c) Find the combination of cars that will cost the least.
State how many of each type of car James and Nicola should hire, and the total cost.

KEY IDEAS

- Inequalities involving the signs $<$ or $>$ are represented on a graph using a dashed line.

- Inequalities involving the signs $\leqslant$ or $\geqslant$ are represented by an unbroken line.

- When representing inequalities like $2x + 3y > 12$ on a graph, first plot the straight line $2x + 3y = 12$ and then decide which side of the line to shade.

- When representing inequalities on a graph, if there is more than one region, it is best to shade the regions not required. This leaves the region required unshaded.

STAGE
8

Cumulative frequency and box plots

You will learn about

- Plotting cumulative frequency diagrams
- Using cumulative frequency diagrams to find the median, quartiles percentiles and the interquartile range
- Using the median, quartiles and interquartile range to draw box plots
- Using the median and interquartile range to analyse data

You should already know

- How to calculate the mode, median, mean and range

Cumulative frequency tables and diagrams

A plant grower wants to find out if one sort of compost is better than another. He sows equal numbers of seeds, from the same packet, in each compost and measures the height, to the nearest centimetre, of 60 plants which grow in each.

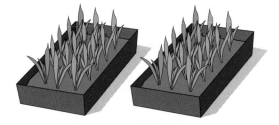

This gives a total of 120 results (60 for each compost), which is a lot to analyse. In cases like this it is better to group the results in intervals. A sensible interval for the heights in this case would be 10 cm.

Compost A

22	13	33	31	24	37	39	28	83	51
31	64	23	35	9	34	42	26	68	38
63	34	44	77	37	15	38	54	34	22
47	25	48	38	53	52	35	45	32	31
37	43	37	49	24	17	48	29	57	33
30	36	42	36	43	38	39	48	39	59

Compost B

33	43	17	50	37	59	21	58	45	78
36	34	45	77	52	42	79	38	63	48
47	71	63	49	8	53	47	66	49	69
55	33	54	28	40	68	55	67	36	76
27	86	29	67	57	47	64	55	48	65
58	41	35	57	44	39	59	23	64	36

This is like sorting the results into 'bins'.

	13	22 24 28	33 31 37 39		
$0 \leqslant h < 10$	$10 \leqslant h < 20$	$20 \leqslant h < 30$	$30 \leqslant h < 40$	$40 \leqslant h < 50$	and so on

Here are the figures for compost A, grouped into a frequency table.

The cumulative frequency in the last column gives the running total. In this case it is the number of plants less than a certain height, for example there are 38 plants less than 40 cm high. Make sure you can see how the cumulative frequency values are obtained.

Height h (cm)	Frequency	Height h (cm)	Cumulative frequency
$h < 0$	0	$h < 0$	0
$0 \leqslant h < 10$	1	$h < 10$	1
$10 \leqslant h < 20$	3	$h < 20$	4
$20 \leqslant h < 30$	9	$h < 30$	13
$30 \leqslant h < 40$	25	$h < 40$	$38 \leftarrow 38 = 1 + 3 + 9 + 25$
$40 \leqslant h < 50$	11	$h < 50$	49
$50 \leqslant h < 60$	6	$h < 60$	55
$60 \leqslant h < 70$	3	$h < 70$	58
$70 \leqslant h < 80$	1	$h < 80$	59
$80 \leqslant h < 90$	1	$h < 90$	60

EXAM TIP

Remember that $\leqslant$ means 'less than or equal to' and $<$ means 'less than' so $30 \leqslant h < 40$ means all the heights between 30 and 40, including 30 but excluding 40.

The values for cumulative frequency can be plotted to give a cumulative frequency diagram.

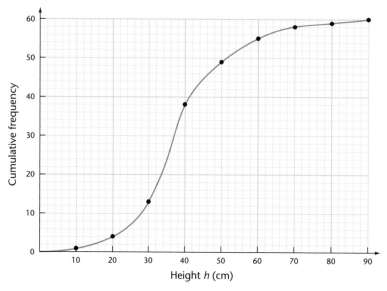

EXAM TIP

In a cumulative frequency diagram, you can join the points with straight (ruled) line segments instead of a curve if you wish.

Note that the cumulative frequency values are plotted at the upper value of each interval, in this case at 10, 20, 30 and so on.

You can use a cumulative frequency diagram to estimate the median value.

There are 60 results so the median will be the 30th value, which is halfway.

Note: If you were using a list of values, then for an even number of values the median would be halfway between the two middle values.

Find 30 on the vertical scale and look across the graph until you reach the curve. Read off the corresponding value on the horizontal scale.

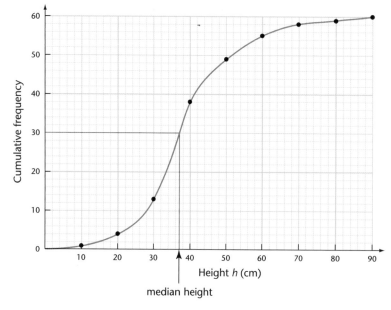

The median height is about 37 cm; check you agree.

It is also possible to calculate the quartiles. As the name suggests these are quarters: the cumulative frequency is divided into four equal parts. The median is the middle quartile. The lower quartile will be at $\frac{1}{4}$ of 60, which is the 15th value, giving a height of 31 cm.

The upper quartile is at $\frac{3}{4}$ of 60, which is the 45th value, giving a height of 45 cm.

Other names for the lower quartile are the 25th percentile or Q_1. Other names for median are the 50th percentile or Q_2. Other names for the upper quartile are the 75th percentile or Q_3. The difference between the upper and lower quartiles is called the **interquartile range**.

Interquartile range = 45 cm – 31 cm = 14 cm

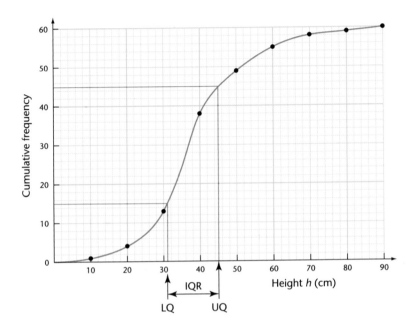

The interquartile range shows how widely the data are spread out. Half the data are within the interquartile range, and if that range is small then the data are bunched together.

STAGE
8

You can also use the cumulative frequency diagram to estimate how many plants were taller than a given height, such as 55 cm. From the graph, a height of 55 cm corresponds to a cumulative frequency of 52, so the number of plants that were taller than 55 cm is $60 - 52 = 8$.

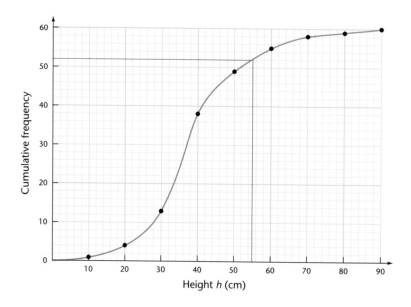

A ACTIVITY 1

a) Construct a grouped frequency table and find the cumulative frequency for the plant heights for compost B.

b) Copy the cumulative frequency diagram for compost A.
Using the same axes, draw the cumulative frequency diagram for compost B and calculate the median value and the interquartile range.

c) Compare the results for the two composts, writing down what you notice.

C CHALLENGE 1

Construct a grouped frequency table and draw a cumulative frequency diagram for a survey or an experiment of your own choice.

Calculate the median value and the Interquartile range.

Write up your findings.

Box plots

Look again at the results for the two composts.

	Lowest value	Lower quartile	Median	Upper quartile	Highest value
A	9	31	37	45	83
B	8	38	49	61	86

These figures can be shown in a diagram called a **box plot**.

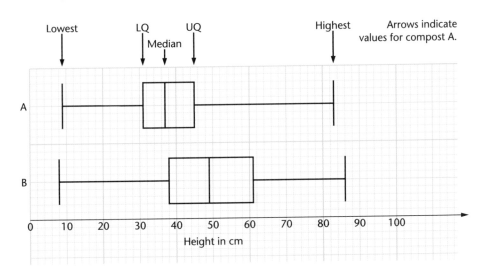

The rectangular 'box' goes from the lower quartile to the upper quartile with a line drawn through the median. The width of the box represents the interquartile range. The lines, sometimes called 'whiskers', extend from the smallest value to the lower quartile and from the upper quartile to the highest value.

These plots give a very quick visual comparison of the two sets of figures. It can be clearly seen that the median for B is higher. The fact that the 'box' for B is wider indicates that B has a wider spread of values.

When information is grouped and the raw scores are not available, it is often difficult to say what the highest and lowest values are. In this case estimates have to be made.

STAGE

8

> ### EXAM TIP
> If you are drawing a cumulative frequency diagram and the question also asks for a box plot, it is a good idea to leave space below the horizontal axis for the box plot.

EXERCISE 7.1

1 The cumulative frequency diagram below shows the masses of 160 boys and 160 girls in a sixth form college.

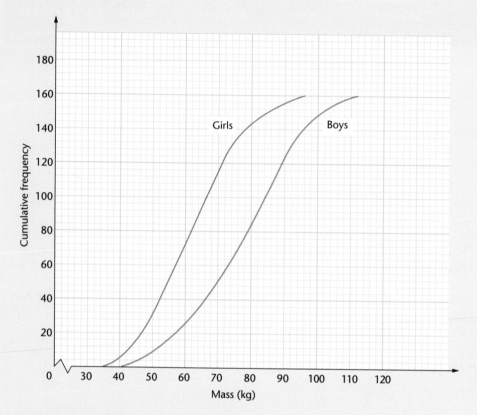

a) Use the diagram to find the medians, quartiles and interquartile ranges for both the boys and the girls.

b) Draw box plots for both the boys and the girls.

2 The diagram shows a box plot for the marks obtained in an examination.

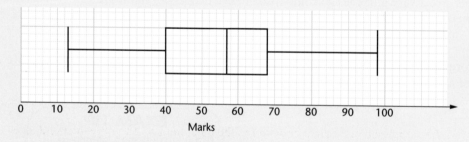

Use the box plot to find these statistics for the distribution of marks.

a) The median

b) The range

c) The interquartile range

3 The table shows the yield, in litres of milk, produced by 120 cows at a certain farm on a certain day.

Yield in litres (x)	Number of cows
$x \leqslant 5$	0
$5 < x \leqslant 10$	10
$10 < x \leqslant 15$	23
$15 < x \leqslant 20$	35
$20 < x \leqslant 25$	26
$25 < x \leqslant 30$	17
$30 < x \leqslant 35$	9

a) Make a cumulative frequency table for the data and use it to draw a cumulative frequency diagram. Use a scale of 2 cm to 5 litres on the horizontal axis and 2 cm to 20 cows on the vertical axis.

b) Use the diagram to find the median, quartiles and interquartile range for the data.

c) Draw a box plot to show the figures in part **b)**. Assume a minimum yield of 5 litres and a maximum yield of 35 litres.

4 The table shows the times taken for the 200 runners in a half-marathon.

Time in minutes (t)	Number of runners
$t \leqslant 60$	0
$60 < t \leqslant 80$	10
$80 < t \leqslant 100$	37
$100 < t \leqslant 120$	72
$120 < t \leqslant 140$	55
$140 < t \leqslant 160$	18
$160 < t \leqslant 180$	7
$180 < t \leqslant 200$	1

a) Make a cumulative frequency table for the data and use it to draw a cumulative frequency diagram. Use a scale of 2 cm to 20 minutes on the horizontal axis and 2 cm to 20 people on the vertical axis.

b) Use the diagram to find the median, quartiles and interquartile range for the data.

c) Draw a box plot to show the figures in part **b)**. Assume a minimum time of 60 minutes and a maximum time of 200 minutes.

STAGE

8

5 The table shows the heights of 120 people.

Height in cm (h)	Number of people
$h \leqslant 130$	0
$130 < h \leqslant 140$	5
$140 < h \leqslant 150$	12
$150 < h \leqslant 160$	26
$160 < h \leqslant 170$	35
$170 < h \leqslant 180$	23
$180 < h \leqslant 190$	15
$190 < h \leqslant 200$	4

a) Make a cumulative frequency table for the data and use it to draw a cumulative frequency diagram. Use a scale of 2 cm to 10 cm on the horizontal axis and 2 cm to 20 people on the vertical axis.

b) Use the diagram to find the median, quartiles and interquartile range for the data.

c) Draw a box plot to show the figures in part **b)**. Assume a minimum height of 130 cm and a maximum height of 200 cm.

6 The lengths, in hours, of lives of 90 light bulbs, were measured and the results recorded in the following table.

Height in hours (t)	Number of bulbs
$t \leqslant 600$	0
$600 < t \leqslant 625$	3
$625 < t \leqslant 650$	18
$650 < t \leqslant 675$	29
$675 < t \leqslant 700$	25
$700 < t \leqslant 725$	13
$725 < t \leqslant 750$	2

a) Make a cumulative frequency table for the data and use it to draw a cumulative frequency diagram. Use a scale of 2 cm to 20 hours on the horizontal axis and 2 cm to 20 bulbs on the vertical axis.

b) Use the diagram to find the median, quartiles and interquartile range for the data.

c) Draw a box plot to show the figures in part **b)**. Assume a minimum life of 600 hours and a maximum life of 750 hours.

7 The table on the left shows information about the masses of 200 potatoes.

a) Copy and complete the cumulative frequency table on the right.

Mass (*m* grams)	Frequency
$0 < m \leqslant 50$	16
$50 < m \leqslant 100$	22
$100 < m \leqslant 150$	43
$150 < m \leqslant 200$	62
$200 < m \leqslant 250$	40
$250 < m \leqslant 300$	13
$300 < m \leqslant 350$	4

Mass (*m* grams)	Cumulative frequency
$m \leqslant 0$	0
$m \leqslant 50$	16
$m \leqslant 100$	38
$m \leqslant 150$	
$m \leqslant 200$	
$m \leqslant 250$	
$m \leqslant 300$	
$m \leqslant 350$	

b) Draw the cumulative frequency diagram.

c) Use your diagram to find the median and interquartile range of these masses.

8 Here is a summary for a distribution of marks gained by a year-group in an examination.

Minimum (Q_0)	LQ (Q_1)	Median (Q_2)	UQ (Q_3)	Maximum (Q_4)
23	52	65	73	98

Draw a box plot for this distribution.

9 The table on the left shows the ages of people in a netball club.

a) Copy and complete the cumulative frequency table on the right.

Age (years)	Frequency
10–15	7
16–18	10
19–24	15
25–34	20
35–49	12
50–64	7

Age (y years)	Cumulative frequency
$y < 10$	0
$y < 16$	7
$y < 19$	17
$y <$	
$y <$	

Note: the upper boundary of the 10–15 age group is the 16th birthday.

b) Draw the cumulative frequency diagram.

c) How many people in this club are aged under 30?

d) How many people in this club are aged 40 or over?

e) Find the median and the quartiles.

10 This table shows the earnings for a group of students in one week.

Earnings (£w)	$0 < w \leqslant 20$	$20 < w \leqslant 40$	$40 < w \leqslant 60$	$60 < w \leqslant 80$	$80 < w \leqslant 100$
Frequency	5	15	26	30	6

Draw a cumulative frequency diagram and a box plot to represent this distribution.

STAGE 8

K KEY IDEAS

- Grouped data are used when there are a lot of results to analyse.

- Cumulative frequency diagrams are useful for estimating the interquartile range and median of a set of data.

- Distributions can be compared using box plots.

Repeated percentage and proportionate change

You will learn about

- Calculating repeated percentage increase and decrease
- Calculating repeated proportionate increase and decrease
- Using these in practical problems such as compound interest and depreciation

You should already know

- How to calculate with decimals, fractions and percentages
- How to calculate percentage increase and decrease

Repeated percentage increases

You found in Chapter 5 that a quick way of increasing by, for example 18%, is to multiply by 1·18. Similarly to increase by 7%, a quick way is to multiply by 1·07.

This method is particularly useful when doing repeated increases.

EXAMPLE 1

Due to inflation, prices increase by 5% per year. An item costs £12 now. What will it cost in 2 years' time?

In 1 year the price will be £12 × 1·05 = £12·60.

In 2 years the price will be £12·60 × 1·05 = £13·23.

Alternatively, this repeated calculation could be worked out as

£12 × 1·05 × 1·05 = £13·23.

EXAMPLE 2

Selena invested £4000 and received 5% interest a year which was added on each year. How much had she in total after

a) 1 year?

b) 6 years?

A 5% increase means that the new amount is 100 + 5 = 105% of the old amount each year.

105% is 1·05, so multiply by 1·05 each year.

a) After one year the total amount is £4000 × 1·05 = £4200.

b) After 6 years the total amount is

$4000 \times 1.05 \times 1.05 \times 1.05 \times 1.05 \times 1.05 \times 1.05$
$= 4000 \times (1.05)^6$
$= £5360.38$ (to the nearest penny).

On a calculator, the calculation for Example 2 b) can be done using the power key. This is usually labelled $\boxed{^\wedge}$ but may be labelled $\boxed{y^x}$ or $\boxed{x^y}$.

The calculation is then simply $\boxed{4}\boxed{0}\boxed{0}\boxed{0}\boxed{\times}\boxed{1}\boxed{.}\boxed{0}\boxed{5}\boxed{^\wedge}\boxed{6}\boxed{=}$ £5360·38.

Example 2 is an example of calculating **compound interest**. Compound interest is added on to what was in the bank at the beginning of the year. So each year the interest increases. In contrast, if the investment only received **simple interest**, the £200 interest received in the first year would be the same for every year.

Repeated percentage decreases

Repeated percentage decreases are calculated in a similar way.

EXAMPLE 3

Each year a car loses value by 12% of its value at the beginning of the year.
If its starting value was £9000 find its value after 3 years.

$100\% - 12\% = 88\%$

$$\begin{aligned}
\text{So after 1 year the value} &= £9000 \times 0{\cdot}88 \\
&= £7920 \\
\text{after 2 years the value} &= £7920 \times 0{\cdot}88 \\
&= £6969{\cdot}60 \\
\text{after 3 years the value} &= £6969{\cdot}60 \times 0{\cdot}88 \\
&= £6133{\cdot}25 \text{ (to the nearest penny)}
\end{aligned}$$

Alternatively, this repeated calculation could be worked out as

$£9000 \times 0{\cdot}88 \times 0{\cdot}88 \times 0{\cdot}88 = £9000 \times (0{\cdot}88)^3 = £6133{\cdot}25$

When the value of something decreases as in Example 3, it is often called **depreciation**.

EXERCISE 8.1

1   Craig puts £240 into a savings account.
    Each year the savings earn interest at
    6% of the amount in the account at the
    start of the year.
    What will his savings be worth after
    3 years?
    Give your answer to the nearest penny.

2   Calculate the amount each of these
    items is worth if they reduce in value
    by the given percentage for the given
    number of years.

	Original value	% reduction	Number of years
a)	£250	4%	5
b)	£3500	11%	7
c)	£1400	15%	4
d)	£10 500	12%	10

3   Each year a car loses value by 11% of
    its value at the start of the year.
    If it was worth £8000 when it was new,
    what will it be worth after 2 years?

4   Interest of 4% was added to an
    investment of £1500 each year for four
    years.
    How much was it then worth?
    Give the answer to the nearest pound.

5   Calculate the amount that £3000
    invested with compound interest would
    be worth in each of the following cases.
    Give your answers to the nearest penny.
    a)   5% for 4 years
    b)   6% for 20 years
    c)   3·5% for 10 years

STAGE

8

6 Martyn had shares worth £8000.
They increased in value by 7·5%
each year.
What was their value after
10 years?
Give the answer to the nearest pound.

7 A population of bacteria is estimated to
increase by 12% every 24 hours.
The population was 2000 at midnight on
Friday.
What was the population (to the
nearest whole number) by midnight the
following Wednesday?

8 Tony says his narrow boat is increasing
in value by 6% a year.
It was worth £25 000 in 1999.
How much would it be worth, to the
nearest hundred pounds, in 2005 (six
years later) if he is correct?

9 The insurance premium for Della's car
was £360.
The firm reduced it by 12% for each
year she had no claim.
What was the cost after six years with
no claims?
Give the answer to the nearest pound.

10 Sheila joined a keep-fit club that
claimed you would reduce your
running time by 1% each week.
She could run 500 metres in 12 minutes
to start with.
According to the club, how long would
it take her after five weeks?
Give the answer to the nearest second.

11 Mr Costa was offered an 8% rise
every year whilst he worked at the
same firm.
This year he earned £28 500.
How much will he earn after four
rises?
Give the answer to the nearest pound.

12 Mordovia has high inflation.
In 1999 it was 15% a month for the
first six months and 12·5% for the next
six months.

A car cost 78 000 scuds (their unit of
currency) in January 1999.
How much did it cost
a) after six months?
b) in January 2000?
Give the answers to the nearest whole
number.

13 Ambrose invested £3500 in a six-year bond that added 5% to the amount each year for the first three years and 7·5% each year for the next three years.
What is the amount in the bond, to the nearest penny
a) after three years?
b) after six years?

14 Find the difference in interest earned by investing £500 for three years at 12% simple interest or for three years at 10% compound interest.

15 Is it better to invest £1000 for five years at 8% or for four years at 9%?

16 I invest £500 at 7% compound interest.
How many years must I leave it, before it doubles in value?

17 This painting was worth £15 000 in 1998.

The painting increased in value by 15% every year for 6 years.
How much was it worth at the end of the 6 years?
Give your answer to the nearest pound.

18 Tina insures a car with the Suffolk Mutual for fully comprehensive cover for a premium of £463.
The table shows the NCD (No Claims Discount) that she gets if she does not make a claim.
For example, if she does not make a claim for 2 years, there will be a 30% reduction in her premium.

Years without claim	1	2	3	4 or more
Reduction	15%	30%	45%	60%

a) What is the cost of the insurance if she does not make a claim for four years?
b) The Norfolk and East charge the same basic premium of £463 but reduce the premium by 15% each year she does not make a claim. This continues for four years. Which is the cheapest and by how much?

19 Tony invests £250 at an annual interest (compound) rate of 4%.
How many years will it take for the amount to exceed
a) £400?
b) double its original value?

20 The value of a car decreased by 9% per year.
The value when it was new was £14 000. What was its value after 5 years?
Give your answer to the nearest pound.

21 Jane has £5000 pounds to invest. She is looking at these two accounts. They both pay compound interest annually.

Anglo Bank

No Notice Account

4.75%**

**introductory offer reduces to 4.25% after 1 year

Bonus Bank

No Notice Account

4.5%

a) How much would her investment be worth in each of these banks after each of these times?
  (i) 1 year
  (ii) 2 years
  (iii) 3 years

b) Why might Jane prefer to invest in the Anglo Bank?

22 Yassim invested £500 at 4% compound interest.
How many years will it take for the value of his investment to be over £600?

CHALLENGE 1

Paul has £2000 to invest for 6 years.

His bank offers two options: 5% compound interest or 5·5% simple interest.

Which is the better investment?

Show your working.

CHALLENGE 2

a) Investigate how many years it will take for an amount to double at different rates of compound interest.

b) Investigate how many years it will take for the value of an object to halve at various rates of depreciation.

CHALLENGE 3

a) Sarah invested in a bond which increased by 4·5% each year for 5 years.
At the end of that time her bond was worth £10 530·24.
How much did she invest?

b) Joe invests £1000 in a savings account that pays 4·5% compound interest annually.
He invests a further £1000 each year for 4 years.
He then leaves his money in the account for a further 3 years without adding to it.
How much has he in the account at the end of this time?

c) Maria has £12 000 in a savings account that pays 4·75% compound interest annually.
Each year she takes £1000 out of the account immediately after the interest has been added.
(i) After how many years does she first have less than £5000 in her account?
(ii) How much is there then in the account?

Proportionate increases and decreases

Proportionate increases and decreases are worked out in exactly the same way, but fractions are used instead of percentages.

EXAMPLE 4

Andrew said he would increase his giving to charity by $\frac{1}{25}$ each year.
He gave £120 at the start.
How much did he give at the end of the fifth year?

Each year he gave $\frac{26}{25}$ × what he gave in the previous year. $\left(1 + \frac{1}{25} = \frac{26}{25}\right)$

At the end of the fifth year he gave £120 × $\left(\frac{26}{25}\right)^5$.

These are the keys to press.

$$\boxed{1}\,\boxed{2}\,\boxed{0}\,\boxed{\times}\,\boxed{(}\,\boxed{2}\,\boxed{6}\,\boxed{\div}\,\boxed{2}\,\boxed{5}\,\boxed{)}\,\boxed{\wedge}\,\boxed{5}\,\boxed{=}$$

= £145·998
= £146·00 to the nearest penny

STAGE

8

71

EXAMPLE 5

The distance that Patrick can walk in a day is reducing by $\frac{1}{15}$ each year. This year he can walk 12 miles in a day. How far will he be able to walk in five years' time?

The distance reduces by $\frac{1}{15}$ in 1 year, so multiply by $\frac{14}{15}$ for each year.

In five years he will be able to walk $12 \times \left(\frac{14}{15}\right)^5 = 8\cdot499 = 8\cdot50$ miles.

EXERCISE 8.2

1 What do you multiply a quantity by if it is increased by each of these?

a) $\frac{1}{5}$
b) $\frac{2}{9}$
c) $\frac{1}{8}$
d) $\frac{2}{7}$
e) $\frac{1}{6}$
f) $\frac{1}{11}$
g) $\frac{3}{5}$
h) $\frac{3}{7}$

2 What do you multiply a quantity by if it is decreased by each of these?

a) $\frac{1}{5}$
b) $\frac{2}{9}$
c) $\frac{1}{8}$
d) $\frac{2}{7}$
e) $\frac{1}{6}$
f) $\frac{1}{11}$
g) $\frac{3}{5}$
h) $\frac{3}{7}$

3 Calculate the amount each of these items is worth if they increase by the given fraction for the given number of years. Give your answers to the nearest penny.

	Original value	Fraction increase	Number of years
a)	£280	$\frac{1}{5}$	5
b)	£3500	$\frac{1}{8}$	7
c)	£1400	$\frac{2}{9}$	4
d)	£10 500	$\frac{1}{7}$	10

4 Calculate the amount each of these items is worth if they decrease by the given fraction for the given number of years. Give your answers to the nearest penny.

	Original value	Fraction decrease	Number of years
a)	£420	$\frac{1}{6}$	5
b)	£1500	$\frac{2}{5}$	7
c)	£1400	$\frac{1}{9}$	4
d)	£10 500	$\frac{1}{12}$	10

5 At Premda department store they said they would reduce the price of goods still not sold by $\frac{1}{3}$ for each day of the sale.
A coat was offered originally at £65. What was its price after three days, to the nearest penny?

6 Cathy said she would withdraw $\frac{1}{5}$ of the money she had in the bank every time she made a withdrawal. She had £187·50 in the bank to start with.
How much did she have after three withdrawals?

7 An investment firm says it will add $\frac{1}{5}$ to your money each year.
If you invested £3000, how much would it amount to after 10 years? Give the answer to the nearest pound.

EXERCISE 8.2 continued

8 At Patnik shoe shop they offered to decrease the price of a pair of shoes by $\frac{1}{4}$ each day until they were sold. They were priced at £47 to start with. Jean bought them after they had been reduced four times.

How much did she pay? Give the answer to the nearest penny.

9 It is claimed that the number of rabbits in Freeshire is increasing by $\frac{1}{12}$ each year.

It is estimated that there are 1700 rabbits now.

How many will there be after four years if the statement is true? Give the answer to three significant figures.

C CHALLENGE 4

a) Ellie bought a painting for £5000.
During the first year its value increased by $\frac{1}{10}$ and during the second year it increased by $\frac{1}{8}$ of its new value.
What was its value after the two years?

b) Francis invested in a bond.
The value increased by $\frac{1}{20}$ in the first year, but then dropped by $\frac{1}{15}$ of the new value in the second year.
What was the overall fractional increase or decrease of the original value over the two years?

c) The value of a car decreased by $\frac{1}{5}$ each year for five years.
At the end of that time the car was worth £6144.
How much was it worth when new?

d) A canal boat increased in value by $\frac{1}{15}$ each year for two years.
The overall increase was £3100.
What was the original value of the boat?

K KEY IDEAS

- When a quantity is increased by, for example 5% for six years, multiply by 1.05^6.

- When a quantity is reduced by, for example 3% for four years, multiply by 0.97^4.

- When a quantity is increased by a fraction, for example $\frac{1}{10}$ for five years, multiply by $\left(\frac{11}{10}\right)^5$.

- When a quantity is reduced by a fraction, for example $\frac{1}{6}$ for four years, multiply by $\left(\frac{5}{6}\right)^4$.

Revision exercise B1

1   Danielle receives an increase in salary of 4%.
    Her old salary was £17000.
    What will her new salary be?

2   In a sale, all prices are reduced by 15%.
    Find the new price of a pair of trainers that originally cost £65.

3   A headline in a newspaper says 'Petrol prices up 20% in a year'.
    If the price is 95p per litre now, what was the price one year ago?
    Give your answer to the nearest penny.

4   Damien sold his bicycle for £286 at a loss of 45% on what he paid for it.
    How much did he pay?

5   Write down the inequality satisfied by the shaded region in each of these diagrams.

a)

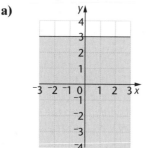

b)

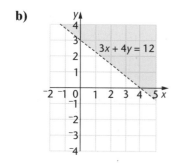

6   Draw sets of axes and label them from $^-4$ to 4 for x and y.
    Shade these regions.
    a) $x \leqslant 1$
    b) $2y < 3x + 2$

7   Draw a set of axes and label them from $^-1$ to 8 for x and y.
    Show, by shading, the region where $x > 0$, $y > 0$, $x < 7$ and $y < x - 1$.

8   Draw a set of axes and label x from $^-1$ to 8 and y from $^-1$ to 5.
    Show, by shading, the region where $x \geqslant 0$, $y \geqslant 0$, $y \leqslant x + 2$ and $3x + 7y \leqslant 21$.

9   In 2005, a small factory employed 200 people.
    The frequency table shows their weekly earnings.

Earnings (£E)	Frequency
$400 < E \leqslant 600$	50
$600 < E \leqslant 800$	55
$800 < E \leqslant 1000$	63
$1000 < E \leqslant 1200$	27
$1200 < E \leqslant 1400$	5

a)   Draw a cumulative frequency diagram of the data.
b)   Use your diagram to find
     (i)   the median earnings.
     (ii)   the interquartile range.
     (iii) the number of employees who earned more then £900 a week.

10 This table shows the numbers of marks obtained by candidates in an examination.

Mark	Number of candidates obtaining less than this mark
10	7
20	16
30	36
40	64
50	102
60	130
70	151
80	162
90	168
100	170

a) Draw a cumulative frequency diagram of the data.

b) Use your diagram to find
   (i) the median mark.
   (ii) the interquartile range.
   (iii) the number of candidates who obtained at least 55 marks.
   (iv) the mark achieved by at least 60% of the candidates.

11 The table shows the age distribution for males (in millions) in England and Wales for two years.

Age	1881	1966
Under 15	4·7	5·6
15 and under 30	3·4	4·9
30 and under 45	2·3	4·4
45 and under 60	1·4	4·4
60 and under 75	0·7	1·7
75 and under 90	0·1	1·7

a) Draw cumulative frequency diagrams for the two years.

b) Use your diagrams to find the medians and quartiles for the two years.

c) Draw box plots for each of the two years using the same axis.
   Assume a minimum age of 0 and a maximum age of 90 for each year.

d) Use your box plots to compare the distributions.

12 Each year the value of an antique increases by 20% of its value at the beginning of the year.
It was worth £450 on 1st January 2003.
a) What was it worth on 1st January 2004?
b) What was it worth on 1st January 2006?

13 A bacterial culture is growing at 5% a day.
There are 1450 bacteria on Tuesday.
How many are there three days later?

14 David invests £5000 in a bank at 4% compound interest.
a) How much will the investment be worth after 5 years?
b) How many years will it take for the investment to be worth £7000?

15 A paper reported that the number of people taking their main holiday in Britain has reduced by 10% every year for the last five years.
There were 560 people from a small town who took their main holiday in Britain five years ago.
If the report is true, how many of them do so now?
Give your answer to the nearest person.

16 A town's road safety campaign aims to reduce accidents by $\frac{1}{8}$ every year for the next three years.
There were 860 accidents last year.
If the campaign is successful, what should the number be reduced to after the three years?

9 Transformations

Reflections

It should be easy to recognise when a transformation is a reflection. If there is any doubt, check that the tracing paper needs to be turned over before it will fit on the image.

To describe a reflection, you need to find and give the mirror line.

▌▌ EXAMPLE 1

Describe the transformation that maps shape ABC on to shape PQR.

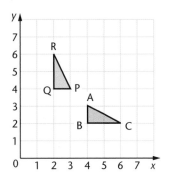

It should be fairly obvious that the transformation is a reflection but this could be checked using tracing paper.

To find the mirror line, put a ruler between two corresponding points (B and Q) and mark a point halfway between them, at (3, 3).

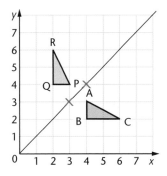

Repeat this for two other corresponding points (C and R). The midpoint is (4, 4).

Join the two midpoints to find the mirror line. The mirror line is $y = x$.

The transformation is a reflection in the line $y = x$.

Again, the result can be checked using tracing paper.

EXAM TIP

Tracing paper is always stated as optional extra material in examinations. When doing transformation questions, always ask for it.

Rotations

It is usually easy to recognise when a transformation is a rotation, as it should be possible to place a tracing of the object over the image without turning the tracing paper over.

To describe a rotation, you need to give the angle of rotation and the centre of rotation.

To find the angle of rotation, find a pair of sides that correspond in the object and the image. Measure the angle between them. You may need to extend both of these sides to do this.

You can usually find the centre of rotation, either by counting squares or using tracing paper.

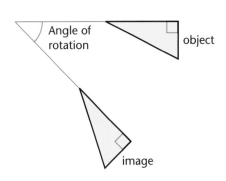

STAGE

8

EXAMPLE 2

Describe fully the transformation that maps triangle A on to triangle B.

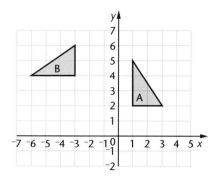

The transformation is a rotation.

The angle is 90° anticlockwise.

You may need to make a few trials, using tracing paper and a compass point centred on different points, to find that the centre of rotation is (⁻2, 1).

EXERCISE 9.1

Label the diagrams you draw in this exercise carefully and keep them as you will need them in a later exercise.

1 **a)** Plot the points $(1, 0)$, $(1, ⁻2)$ and $(2, ⁻2)$ and join them to form a triangle.
        Label it A.
        Reflect triangle A in the line $y = 1$.
        Label the image B.
    b) Reflect triangle B in the line $y = x$.
        Label the image C.

2 **a)** On a new grid, plot the points $(2, 5)$, $(3, 5)$ and $(1, 3)$ and join them to form a triangle.
        Label it D.
        Reflect triangle D in the line $x = \frac{1}{2}$.
        Label the image E.
    b) On the same grid, reflect triangle E in the line $y = ⁻x$.
        Label the image F.

3 **a)** Copy this diagram.

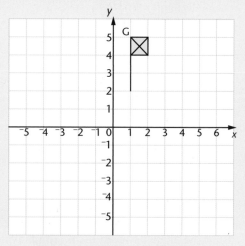

    Rotate the flag G through 90° clockwise about the point $(1, 2)$.
    Label the image H.
    b) On the same grid, rotate the flag H through 180° about the point $(2, ⁻1)$.
    Label the image I.

4 a) Plot the points (0, 1), (0, 4) and (2, 3) and join them to form a triangle.
Label it J.
Rotate triangle J through 90° anticlockwise about the point (2, 3).
Label the image K.

b) On the same grid, rotate triangle K through 90° clockwise about the point (2, ⁻1).
Label the image L.

5 Look at this diagram.

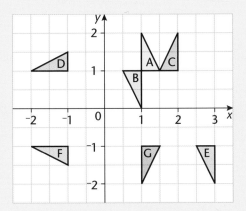

Which of the triangles B, C, D, E, F and G are reflections of triangle A and which are rotations of triangle A?

EXAM TIP

When describing transformations, always state the type of transformation first and then give all the necessary extra information. For reflections this is the mirror line; for rotations it is angle, direction and centre.

You may get no marks unless you actually name the transformation.

6 Look at this diagram.

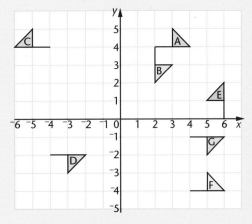

Describe fully these single transformations.
a) Flag A on to flag B
b) Flag A on to flag C
c) Flag B on to flag D
d) Flag B on to flag E
e) Flag E on to flag F
f) Flag F on to flag G

7 Look at this diagram.

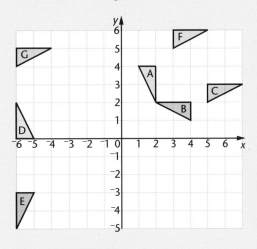

Describe fully these single transformations.
a) Triangle A on to triangle B
b) Triangle A on to triangle C
c) Triangle A on to triangle D
d) Triangle D on to triangle E
e) Triangle E on to triangle F
f) Triangle D on to triangle G

STAGE

8

Translations

In a translation, every point of an object moves the same distance in the same direction. The object and the image look identical with no turning or reflection. It looks just as if the object has moved to a different position.

The movements can be described as a movement in the x-direction and a movement in the y-direction. They can be written in the form of a column vector, for example $\begin{pmatrix} 5 \\ -3 \end{pmatrix}$.

In a column vector, the top number represents the x-movement and the bottom number represents the y-movement.

The directions are the same as for coordinates.
If the top number is positive, move to the right.
If the top number is negative, move to the left.
If the bottom number is positive, move up.
If the bottom number is negative, move down.

To find the column vector, identify a point on the object and the corresponding point on the image. Count how many units left or right and how many units up or down that point has moved. Write these movements as a column vector.

EXAMPLE 3

Describe fully the transformation that maps triangle ABC on to triangle PQR.

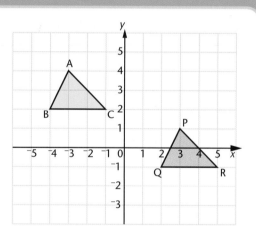

Point A is translated on to point P. This is a movement of 6 to the right and 3 down. The transformation is a translation by the vector $\begin{pmatrix} 6 \\ -3 \end{pmatrix}$.

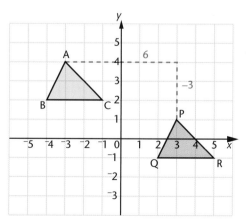

EXAM TIP

Try not to mix up the words 'transformation' and 'translation'. Transformation is the general name for all the changes made to shapes. Translation is the particular transformation that has been described here.

Enlargements

An **enlargement** produces an image that is exactly similar in shape to the object, but is larger or smaller.

Drawing enlargements

▌▌EXAMPLE 4

Enlarge the triangle ABC with scale factor 2·5 and centre of enlargement O, to form triangle PQR.

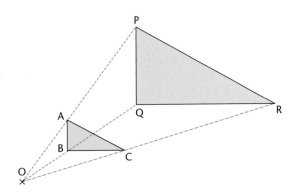

Draw lines from O to A, O to B and O to C and extend them.

Measure the lengths OA, OB and OC. These are 2·0 cm, 1·5 cm and 2·9 cm respectively.

Multiply these lengths by 2·5 to give OP = 5·0 cm, OQ = 3·75 cm and OR = 7·25 cm.

Measure these distances along the extended lines OA, OB and OC, and mark P, Q and R.

Join P, Q and R to form the triangle.

EXAM TIP

When you have drawn your enlargement, check that the ratio of the sides of the image to the corresponding sides in the object is equal to the scale factor (in the case of Example 4, 2·5).

If it is not, you have probably measured some or all of your distances from the points of the object and not from O.

STAGE
8

Negative scale factors

If the scale factor of an enlargement is negative, the image is on the opposite side of the centre of enlargement from the object, and the image is inverted. This is shown in the next example.

EXAMPLE 5

Plot the coordinates A(2, 2), B(4, 2) and C(2, 5) and join them to form a triangle.

Enlarge triangle ABC by a scale factor of ⁻3 using the point O(1, 1) as the centre of enlargement.

Plot the triangle.

Then draw a line from each of the vertices through the centre of enlargement O and extend it on the other side.

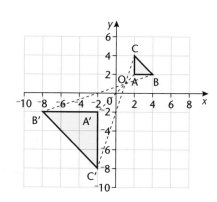

Measure the distance from the vertex A and multiply it by 3.

Then mark the point A′ at a distance of 3 × OA along OA extended on the other side of the centre of enlargement.

Repeat this for points B and C, labelling the images B′ and C′.

Notice that the image is on the opposite side of O.
It is three times the size of the object ABC and is inverted.

EXAM TIP

You can find the position of the image points by counting squares from the centre of enlargement as you have done previously, so long as you remember the image will be on the opposite side from the object.

For example, from the centre of enlargement to point B is 3 units in the positive *x*-direction and 1 unit in the positive *y*-direction. Multiplying by the scale factor, point B′ is 9 units in the negative *x*-direction and 3 units in the negative *y*-direction.

Describing enlargements

To describe an enlargement, you need to give the scale factor of the enlargement and the centre of the enlargement.

To find the scale factor, measure corresponding sides and divide the length of the side on the image by the length of the side on the object.

To find the centre of enlargement, join corresponding points on the two shapes with straight lines. The centre of enlargement is where the lines cross.

EXAMPLE 6

Describe fully the transformation that maps triangle DEF on to triangle STU.

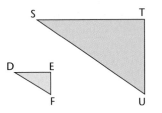

The shapes are similar, so the transformation is an enlargement.

Since the lengths of the sides of triangle STU are 3 times the lengths of the corresponding sides of triangle DEF, the scale factor is 3.

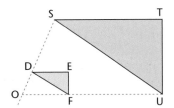

All that remains to be found is the centre of enlargement. Join SD and extend it. Join UF and extend it to cross the extended line SD. The point where the lines cross, O, is the centre of enlargement.

The transformation is an enlargement, scale factor 3, centre of enlargement O.

If you were working on a grid, you would describe the centre of enlargement by stating the coordinates of the point.

The transformation that maps triangle STU on to triangle DEF in Example 6 is an enlargement with centre O and a scale factor of $\frac{1}{3}$. Note that it is still called an enlargement even though the image is smaller than the object.

EXERCISE 9.2

Label the diagrams you draw in this exercise carefully and keep them as you will need them in a later exercise.

1 **a)** Plot the points (1, 2), (1, 4) and (2, 4) and join them to form a triangle. Label it A. Translate triangle A by the vector $\begin{pmatrix} 5 \\ 2 \end{pmatrix}$. Label the image B.

   b) On the same grid, translate triangle B by the vector $\begin{pmatrix} 2 \\ -4 \end{pmatrix}$. Label the image C.

2 **a)** On a new grid, plot the points (0, 2), (1, 4) and (3, 2) and join them to form a triangle. Label it D. Translate triangle D by the vector $\begin{pmatrix} -4 \\ 2 \end{pmatrix}$. Label it E.

   b) On the same grid, translate triangle E by the vector $\begin{pmatrix} 8 \\ 0 \end{pmatrix}$. Label the image F.

3 **a)** Draw a set of axes. Label the *x*-axis from 0 to 13 and the *y*-axis from 0 to 15.
Plot the points (1, 2), (2, 4) and (1, 3) and join them to form a triangle. Label it G.
Enlarge triangle G with scale factor 2 and centre the origin. Label the image H.

b) On the same grid, enlarge triangle H with scale factor 3 and centre of enlargement (0, 5). Label the image I.

4 **a)** Copy the diagram.

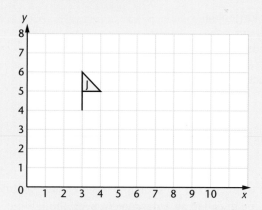

Enlarge the flag J with scale factor 1·5 and centre of enlargement (1, 2). Label the image K.

b) On the same grid, enlarge the flag K with scale factor 2 and centre of enlargement (2, 8). Label the image L.

5 Draw a set of axes, the *x*-axis from ⁻16 to 6 and the *y*-axis from ⁻8 to 4.
Plot the points A(2, 2), B(5, 0), C(5, ⁻1), D(2, ⁻1) and join them to form a quadrilateral.
Enlarge this quadrilateral with scale factor ⁻3 and centre of enlargement the origin.

6 Draw a set of axes, the *x*-axis from ⁻16 to 6 and the *y*-axis from ⁻8 to 4.
Plot the points P(4, 2), Q(6, ⁻1), R(2, ⁻2) and join them to form a triangle.
Enlarge this triangle with scale factor ⁻2 and centre of enlargement the origin.

7 Draw a set of axes, the *x*-axis from ⁻14 to 6 and the *y*-axis from ⁻8 to 4.
Plot the points A(2, ⁻2), B(5, 1), C(2, 2) and join them to form a triangle.
Enlarge this triangle with scale factor ⁻2 and centre of enlargement (⁻1, ⁻1).
Write down the coordinates of the image.

8 Draw a set of axes, the *x*-axis from 0 to 10 and the *y*-axis from 0 to 8.
Plot the points A(1, 6), B(1, 7), C(3, 7) and join them to form a triangle.
Enlarge this triangle with scale factor ⁻3 and centre of enlargement (3, 6).
Write down the coordinates of the image.

9 Look at this diagram.

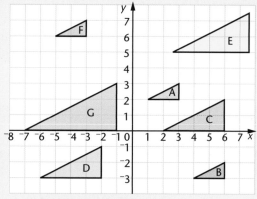

Describe fully these single transformations.
a) Triangle A on to triangle B
b) Triangle A on to triangle C
c) Triangle C on to triangle D
d) Triangle A on to triangle E
e) Triangle A on to triangle F
f) Triangle G on to triangle A

EXERCISE 9.2 continued

10 Look at this diagram.

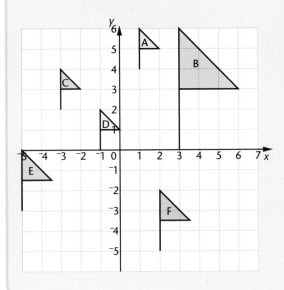

Describe fully these single transformations.
- **a)** Flag A on to flag B
- **b)** Flag A on to flag C
- **c)** Flag C on to flag D
- **d)** Flag D on to flag E
- **e)** Flag E on to flag F
- **f)** Flag B on to flag D

C CHALLENGE 1

A triangle ABC has sides AB = 9 cm, AC = 7 cm and BC = 6 cm.

A line XY is drawn parallel to BC through a point X on AB and a point Y on AC.

AX = 5 cm.

a) Draw a sketch of the triangles.

b) (i) Describe fully the transformation that maps ABC on to AXY.
 (ii) Work out the length of XY correct to 2 decimal places.

STAGE

8

Combining transformations

Sometimes when one transformation is followed by another, the result is equivalent to a single transformation.

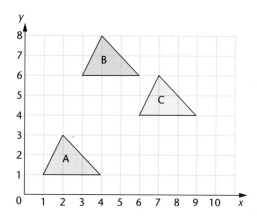

For example, in the diagram, triangle A has been translated by the vector $\begin{pmatrix} 2 \\ 5 \end{pmatrix}$ on to triangle B.

Triangle B has then been translated by the vector $\begin{pmatrix} 3 \\ -2 \end{pmatrix}$ on to triangle C.

Notice that triangle A could have been translated directly on to triangle C by the vector $\begin{pmatrix} 5 \\ 3 \end{pmatrix}$.

So the first transformation followed by the second transformation is equivalent to the single transformation: translation by the vector $\begin{pmatrix} 5 \\ 3 \end{pmatrix}$.

EXAM TIP

Make sure you do the transformations in the right order, as it usually makes a difference.

If a question asks for a single transformation, do not give a combination of two transformations as this does not answer the question and will usually score no marks.

STAGE
8

EXAMPLE 7

Find the single transformation that is equivalent to a reflection in the line $x = 1$, followed by a reflection in the line $y = {}^-2$.

Choose a simple shape and draw a diagram. An asymmetrical shape such as a right-angled triangle or a flag is usually best.

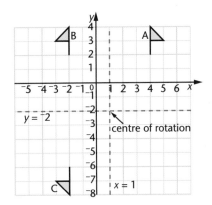

In the diagram, reflecting the object flag A in the line $x = 1$ gives flag B.

Reflecting flag B in the line $y = {}^-2$ gives flag C.

The transformation that maps A directly on to C is a rotation through 180°.

The centre of rotation is $(1, {}^-2)$, which is where the mirror lines cross.

The transformation is a rotation through 180° about the centre of rotation $(1, {}^-2)$.

Use tracing paper to check this.

A rotation of 180° is the only rotation for which you do not need to state the direction, as 180° clockwise is the same as 180° anticlockwise.

EXERCISE 9.3

In this exercise you will need some of the diagrams you drew in Exercises 9.1 and 9.2.

1   Look back at the diagram you drew for question **1** of Exercise 9.2. Describe fully the single transformation that is equivalent to a translation by the vector $\begin{pmatrix} 5 \\ 2 \end{pmatrix}$ (A on to B) followed by a translation by the vector $\begin{pmatrix} 2 \\ -4 \end{pmatrix}$ (B on to C).

2   Look back at the diagram you drew for question **2** of Exercise 9.2. Describe fully the single transformation that is equivalent to a translation by the vector $\begin{pmatrix} -4 \\ 2 \end{pmatrix}$ (D on to E) followed by a translation by the vector $\begin{pmatrix} 8 \\ 0 \end{pmatrix}$ (E on to F).

3   Look back at the diagram you drew for question **3** of Exercise 9.2. Describe fully the single transformation that is equivalent to an enlargement, scale factor 2, centre the origin (G on to H) followed by an enlargement scale factor 3, centre $(0, 5)$ (H on to I).

4   Look back at the diagram you drew for question **4** of Exercise 9.2. Describe fully the single transformation that is equivalent to an enlargement, scale factor $1\frac{1}{2}$, centre the point $(1, 2)$ (J on to K) followed by an enlargement, scale factor 2, centre $(2, 8)$ (K on to L).

5 Look back at the diagram you drew for question **1** of Exercise 9.1. Describe fully the single transformation that is equivalent to a reflection in the line $y = 1$ (A on to B) followed by a reflection in the line $y = x$ (B on to C).

6 Look back at the diagram you drew for question **2** of Exercise 9.1. Describe fully the single transformation that is equivalent to a reflection in the line $x = \frac{1}{2}$ (D on to E) followed by a reflection in the line $y = ^-x$ (E on to F).

7 Look back at the diagram you drew for question **3** of Exercise 9.1. Describe fully the single transformation that is equivalent to a rotation through 90° clockwise about the point (1, 2) (G on to H) followed by a rotation through 180° about the point (2, ⁻1) (H on to I).

8 Look back at the diagram you drew for question **4** of Exercise 9.1. Describe fully the single transformation that is equivalent to a rotation through 90° anticlockwise about the point (2, 3) (J on to K) followed by a rotation through 90° clockwise about the point (2, ⁻1) (K on to L).

9 Copy the diagram.

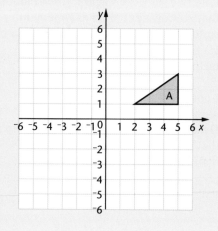

a) Reflect triangle A in the *x*-axis. Label the image B.
b) Reflect triangle B in the *y*-axis. Label the image C.
c) Describe fully the single transformation that will map triangle A on to triangle C.

In questions **10** to **16**, carry out the transformations on a simple shape of your choice.

10 Describe fully the single transformation that is equivalent to a reflection in the line $x = 1$ followed by a reflection in the line $x = 5$.

11 Describe fully the single transformation that is equivalent to a reflection in the line $y = 2$ followed by a reflection in the line $y = 6$.

12 Describe fully the single transformation that is equivalent to an enlargement, scale factor 2 and centre the origin, followed by a translation by the vector $\begin{pmatrix} 3 \\ 2 \end{pmatrix}$.

13 Describe fully the single transformation that is equivalent to a rotation through 90° clockwise about the origin, followed by a translation by the vector $\begin{pmatrix} 4 \\ 0 \end{pmatrix}$.

14 Describe fully the single transformation that is equivalent to a reflection in the *x*-axis followed by a rotation through 90° anticlockwise about the origin.

15 Describe fully the single transformation that is equivalent to a reflection in the *y*-axis followed by a rotation through 90° anticlockwise about the origin.

16 Describe fully the single transformation that is equivalent to a reflection in the line $y = x$ followed by a reflection in the line $y = ^-x$.

CHALLENGE 2

Look at your answers to Exercise 9.3 questions **10** and **11**.

Try to make a general statement about the result of reflection in a mirror line followed by reflection in a parallel mirror line.

CHALLENGE 3

Look at the answers to Exercise 9.3 questions **5** and **6**.

Try to make a general statement about the result of reflection in a mirror line followed by reflection in an intersecting mirror line.

CHALLENGE 4

Draw a pair of axes and label them ⁻6 to 6 for x and y.

a) Draw a shape in the positive region near the origin. Label it A.

b) Translate shape A by vector $\begin{pmatrix} 2 \\ 1 \end{pmatrix}$. Label it B.

c) Translate shape B by vector $\begin{pmatrix} 3 \\ -2 \end{pmatrix}$. Label it C.

d) Translate shape C by vector $\begin{pmatrix} -6 \\ -1 \end{pmatrix}$. Label it D.

e) Translate shape D by vector $\begin{pmatrix} 1 \\ 2 \end{pmatrix}$. Label it E.

f) What do you notice about shapes A and E? Can you suggest why this happens? Try to find other combinations of translations for which this happens.

CHALLENGE 5

Look at your answers to Exercise 9.3, questions **1** and **2**.

Try to make a general statement about the result of translation by the vector

$\begin{pmatrix} a \\ b \end{pmatrix}$ followed by translation by the vector $\begin{pmatrix} c \\ d \end{pmatrix}$.

STAGE
8

C CHALLENGE 6

Look again at the answers to Exercise 9.3, questions **3** and **4**.

Try to make a general statement about the result of enlargement with scale factor p followed by enlargement with scale factor q.

K KEY IDEAS

■ When describing transformations, always give the name of the transformation and then the extra information required.

Name of transformation	Extra information
Reflection	Mirror line
Rotation	Angle, direction, centre of rotation
Translation	Column vector
Enlargement	Scale factor, centre of enlargement

■ When asked to describe a single transformation, do not give a combination of transformations.

STAGE
8

Simultaneous equations

You will learn about

- Solving simultaneous equations graphically
- Solving simultaneous equations algebraically
- Solving problems which lead to simultaneous equations

You should already know

- How to draw graphs of linear equations such as
  $y = 3x - 2$ and $3x + 2y = 12$
- How to add and subtract simple algebraic expressions
- How to write a formula using letters
- How to rearrange equations

An equation in two unknowns does not have a unique solution. For example, the graph of the equation $x + y = 4$ is a straight line. Every point on the line will have coordinates that satisfy the equation.

When you are given two equations in two unknowns, such as x and y, they usually have a common solution where the two lines meet at a point. These are called *simultaneous equations*.

The graphical method of solving simultaneous equations

One way to solve simultaneous linear equations is to use a graph. The point(s) where the lines or curves meet will give the solution.

STAGE
8

EXAMPLE 1

Solve the simultaneous equations $y = 2x - 4$ and $3y = 12 - 2x$ graphically.
Use values of x from 0 to 6.

Three points for $y = 2x - 4$ are $(0, {}^{-}4)$, $(3, 2)$, $(6, 8)$.
Three points for $3y = 12 - 2x$ are $(0, 4)$, $(3, 2)$, $(6, 0)$.

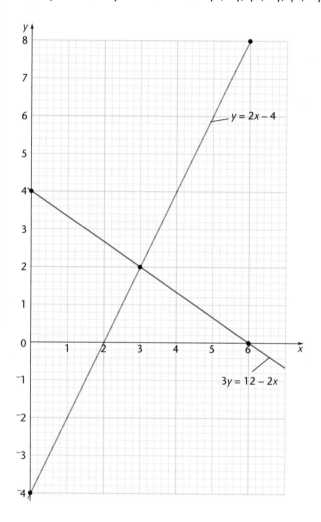

The two lines cross at $(3, 2)$.
Since this point is on both lines, the coordinates satisfy both equations, so the solution
is $x = 3$, $y = 2$.

EXERCISE 10.1

Solve these simultaneous equations graphically.

1 $y = 2x$ and $y = 8 - 2x$.
On graph paper, draw a set of axes with values of x from $^-1$ to 4 and values of y from $^-2$ to 10.

2 $y = 3x$ and $y = 4x - 2$.
On graph paper, draw a set of axes with values of x from $^-3$ to 3 and values of y from $^-10$ to 10.

3 $y = 3x + 5$ and $y = x + 3$.
On graph paper, draw a set of axes with values of x from $^-3$ to 2 and values of y from $^-4$ to 11.

4 $y = 2x + 3$ and $y = 4x + 1$.
On graph paper, draw a set of axes with values of x from $^-2$ to 3 and values of y from $^-7$ to 13.

5 $y = 5 - x$ and $y = 2x - 7$.
On graph paper, draw a set of axes with values of x from $^-1$ to 5 and values of y from $^-8$ to 6.

6 $y = x + 4$ and $4x + 3y = 12$.
On graph paper, draw a set of axes with values of x from $^-3$ to 3 and values of y from 0 to 8.

7 $2y = 2x + 1$ and $2y + x = 7$.
On graph paper, draw a set of axes with values of x and y from $^-2$ to 8.

8 $y = 2x + 8$ and $y = ^-2x$.
On graph paper, draw a set of axes with values of x from $^-5$ to 1 and values of y from $^-2$ to 10.

Solving simultaneous equations by the method of elimination

The main problems with solving simultaneous equations graphically are the time it takes and the fact that you do not always obtain accurate solutions.

It is often preferable, therefore, to solve them accurately using algebra.

If two quantities A and B are equal and two other quantities C and D are equal, it follows logically that

$$A + C = B + D$$
and $\quad A - C = B - D$

Therefore you can add the left-hand sides of two simultaneous equations and the result will equal the two right-hand sides added together.

Similarly you can subtract the left-hand sides of two simultaneous equations and the result will equal the two right-hand sides subtracted.

This is shown in the following examples.

EXAMPLE 2

Solve the simultaneous equations $x + y = 4$ and $2x - y = 5$.

$x + y = 4$ (1)   Write the two equations, one under the other, and label them.
$2x - y = 5$ (2)

Look to see if either of the unknowns (x or y) has the same coefficient in both equations. In this case there is $1y$ in equation (1) and $1y$ in equation (2). As their signs are different, the two y-terms will be eliminated (cancel each other out) if the two equations are added.

$x + 2x + y + (^-y) = 4 + 5$ Adding (1) and (2).
$3x = 9$
$x = 3$

To find the value of y, substitute $x = 3$ in equation (1).

$3 + y = 4$ Replacing x by 3.
$y = 1$

So the solution is $x = 3$, $y = 1$.

Check in equation (2): the left-hand side is $2x - y = 6 - 1 = 5$ which is correct.

EXAMPLE 3

Solve the simultaneous equations $2x + 5y = 9$ and $2x - y = 3$.

$2x + 5y = 9$ (1)   Set out in line.
$2x - y = 3$ (2)

This time $(^+)2x$ appears in each equation, so subtract to eliminate the x-terms.

$2x - 2x + 5y - (^-y) = 9 - 3$ (1) − (2). Take care with the signs. $5y - (^-y) = 5y + y$.
$6y = 6$
$y = 1$

$2x + 5 = 9$ Substitute $y = 1$ in (1): $5y$ is replaced by $5 \times 1 = 5$.
$2x = 4$
$x = 2$

The solution is $x = 2$, $y = 1$.

Check in equation (2): the left-hand side is $2x - y = 4 - 1 = 3$ which is correct.

EXAM TIP

When eliminating, if the signs of the letter to be eliminated are the same, subtract. If they are different, add.

When subtracting, take great care with the signs. This is where most errors are made. If your check is wrong, see if you have made an error with any signs.

EXAMPLE 4

Solve the simultaneous equations $x + 3y = 10$ and $3x + 2y = 16$.

$$x + 3y = 10 \quad (1)$$
$$3x + 2y = 16 \quad (2)$$

Set out in line.

This time the coefficients of x and y are different in both equations.

Multiply (1) by 3 to make the coefficient of x the same as in equation (2).

$$3x + 9y = 30 \quad (3)$$
$$3x + 2y = 16 \quad (2)$$

$(1) \times 3$

Now $(^+)3x$ appears in both equations, so subtract.

$$3x - 3x + 9y - 2y = 30 - 16 \quad (3) - (2)$$
$$7y = 14$$
$$y = 2$$

$$x + 6 = 10$$
$$x = 4$$

Substitute in (1).

The solution is $x = 4$, $y = 2$.

Check in equation (2):
the left-hand side is
$3x + 2y = 12 + 4 = 16$
which is correct.

EXAM TIP

When subtracting equations, you can do equation (1) –
equation (2) or equation (2) – equation (1). It is better to
make the letter positive. Always write down clearly what
you are doing.

There is no need to write as much detail as in Example 4.
The next example shows what is required. The
commentary can be omitted.

EXAMPLE 5

Solve simultaneously $4x - y = 10$ and $3x + 2y = 13$.

$$4x - y = 10 \quad (1)$$
$$3x + 2y = 13 \quad (2)$$

Set out in line.

$(1) \times 2 \qquad 8x - 2y = 20 \qquad (3)$ — To get $2y$ in each equation.

$(2) + (3) \quad 3x + 8x + 2y + (^-2y) = 13 + 20$ — To eliminate y.
$$11x = 33$$
$$x = 3$$

Substitute in (1): $\qquad 12 - y = 10$
$$^-y = ^-2$$
$$y = 2$$

The solution is $x = 3$, $y = 2$.

Check in (2): LHS $= 3x + 2y = 9 + 4 = 13$ which is correct.

EXERCISE 10.2

Solve these simultaneous equations.

1 $x + y = 5$
$2x - y = 7$

2 $x + y = 3$
$2x + y = 4$

3 $3x + y = 9$
$2x + y = 7$

4 $2x + y = 6$
$2x - y = 2$

5 $2x + 3y = 11$
$2x + y = 5$

6 $2x - y = 7$
$3x + y = 13$

7 $2x + y = 7$
$4x - y = 5$

8 $2x + y = 12$
$2x - 2y = 6$

9 $2x + 3y = 13$
$3x - 3y = 12$

10 $3x - y = 11$
$3x - 5y = 7$

11 $2x + 3y = 14$
$5x + 3y = 26$

12 $2x + y = 6$
$3x + 2y = 10$

13 $3x + y = 7$
$2x + 3y = 7$

14 $x + 3y = 9$
$2x - y = 4$

15 $2x - 3y = 0$
$3x + y = 11$

16 $x + 2y = 19$
$3x - y = 8$

17 $2x + 3y = 13$
$x + 2y = 8$

18 $x + 2y = 6$
$3x - 3y = 9$

19 $3x + 2y = 13$
$x + 3y = 16$

20 $2x + y = 14$
$3x + 2y = 22$

21 $2x + 3y = 7$
$3x - y = 5$

22 $2x + y = 3$
$3x - 2y = 8$

23 $x + y = 4$
$4x - 2y = 7$

24 $2x + 4y = 11$
$x + 3y = 8$

25 $2x + 2y = 7$
$4x - 3y = 7$

26 $2x - y = 4$
$4x + 3y = 13$

27 $4x - 2y = 14$
$3x + y = 8$

28 $2x - 4y = 2$
$x + 3y = {}^-9$

29 $2x - 2y = 5$
$4x - 3y = 11$

30 $x + y = 0$
$2x + 4y = 3$

Further simultaneous equations

Sometimes the letters in the equations are not in the same order, so the first thing to do is to rearrange them.

EXAMPLE 6

Solve simultaneously the equations $y = 3x - 4$, $x + 2y = {}^-1$.

$$^-3x + y = {}^-4 \qquad (1) \qquad \text{Rearrange the equation.}$$
$$x + 2y = {}^-1 \qquad (2)$$

This can be solved in two ways, either (1) × 2 and subtract or (2) × 3 and add. It is usually easier to add.

$(2) \times 3$
$$3x + 6y = {}^-3 \qquad (3)$$
$$^-3x + y = {}^-4 \qquad (1) \qquad \text{Copy (1) down.}$$

$(3) + (1)$
$$3x + ({}^-3x) + 6y + y = {}^-3 + ({}^-4)$$
$$7y = {}^-7$$
$$y = {}^-1$$

Substitute in (1):
$$^-3x - 1 = {}^-4 \qquad \text{Replace } y \text{ by } {}^-1.$$
$$^-3x = {}^-3$$
$$x = 1$$

The solution is $x = 1$, $y = {}^-1$.

Check in (2): LHS $= x + 2y = 1 - 2 = {}^-1$ which is correct.

Sometimes each of the equations needs to be multiplied by a different number.

STAGE
8

EXAMPLE 7

Solve the equations $3y = 4 - 4x$, $6x + 2y = 11$.

$$4x + 3y = 4 \qquad (1)$$
$$6x + 2y = 11 \qquad (2)$$

Rearrange the first equation.

To eliminate x multiply (1) by 3 and (2) by 2 and subtract, or to eliminate y multiply (1) by 2 and (2) by 3 and subtract.

(1) $\times$ 3	$12x + 9y = 12$	(3)
(2) $\times$ 2	$12x + 4y = 22$	(4)
(3) $-$ (4)	$5y = {}^{-}10$	Eliminate x.
	$y = {}^{-}2$	

Substitute in (1):
$$4x - 6 = 4$$
$$4x = 10$$
$$x = \frac{10}{4} = \frac{5}{2} = 2\frac{1}{2}$$

$3y$ is replaced by $^{-}6$.

The solution is $x = 2\frac{1}{2}$, $y = {}^{-}2$.

Check in (2): LHS $= 6x + 2y = 15 - 4 = 11$ which is correct.

EXAM TIP
If the equations are not already in the form $ax + by = c$, rearrange them so that they are.

EXERCISE 10.3

Solve these simultaneous equations.

1 $y = 2x - 1$
$x + 2y = 8$

2 $3y = 5 - x$
$2x + y = 5$

3 $y = 3 - 2x$
$3x - 3y = 0$

4 $5y = x + 1$
$2x + 2y = 10$

5 $3y = 11 - x$
$3x - y = 3$

6 $y = 3x - 3$
$2x + 3y = 13$

7 $3x + 2y = 7$
$2x - 3y = {}^{-}4$

8 $4x - y = 2$
$5x + 3y = 11$

9 $3x - 2y = 3$
$2x - y = 4$

10 $3x - 2y = 11$
$2x + 3y = 16$

11 $2x + 3y = 7$
$7x - 4y = 10$

12 $2x - 3y = 5$
$3x + 4y = 16$

EXERCISE 10.3 continued

13 $3x + 4y = 5$
$2x + 3y = 4$

14 $2x + 3y = 4$
$3x - 2y = {}^-7$

15 $4x - 3y = 1$
$5x + 2y = {}^-16$

16 $4x + 3y = 1$
$3x + 2y = 0$

17 $3x + 2y = 5$
$2x + 3y = 10$

18 $y = x + 2$
$2x - 4y = {}^-9$

19 $4x - 2y = 3$
$5y = 23 - 3x$

20 $2y = 4x - 5$
$3x - 5y = 9$

> **EXAM TIP**
> If there is a choice whether to add or subtract, it is usually easier to add.

Problems that lead to simultaneous equations

When you are solving real-life problems you will need to write down your own equations.

EXAMPLE 8

In a café, two cups of tea and three cups of coffee cost £5·30. Three cups of tea and one cup of coffee cost £4·10.

Let a cup of tea cost t pence and a cup of coffee cost c pence.

a) Write down two equations in t and c.

b) Solve them to find the cost of a cup of tea and the cost of a cup of coffee.

> **EXAM TIP**
> You should always define the letters you use to stand for quantities and their units if they are not given.

a) $2t + 3c = 530$ (1)   Working in pence.
$3t + c = 410$ (2)

b) (2) × 3 $9t + 3c = 1230$ (3)
             $2t + 3c = 530$ (1)
(3) − (1) $7t = 700$
                  $t = 100$

Substitute in (1): $200 + 3c = 530$
                 $3c = 330$
                   $c = 110$

So tea costs £1 a cup, coffee costs £1·10 a cup.

Check in the problem: 2 teas + 3 coffees cost £2 + £3·30 = £5·30 and 3 teas + 1 coffee cost £3 + £1·10 = £4·10.

STAGE

8

EXERCISE 10.4

1. Two numbers x and y have a sum of 47 and a difference of 9.
   a) Write down two equations in x and y.
   b) Solve them to find the numbers.

2. Two numbers x and y have a sum of 86 and a difference of 16.
   a) Write down two equations in x and y.
   b) Solve them to find the two numbers.

3. Cassettes cost £c each and compact discs cost £d each. John bought two cassettes and three discs and paid £27·50. Shahida bought three cassettes and one disc and paid £18·50.
   a) Write down two equations in c and d.
   b) Solve them to find the cost of a cassette and of a disc.

4. At Turner's corner shop beans cost b pence a tin and spaghetti costs s pence a tin. Three tins of beans and two tins of spaghetti cost £1·37. Two tins of beans and a tin of spaghetti cost 81p.
   a) Write down two equations in b and s.
   b) Solve them to find the cost of each tin.

5. Paint is sold in small and large tins. Peter needs 13 litres and he buys one small and two large tins. Gamel needs 11 litres and he buys two small and one large tin. Both have exactly the correct amount.
   Let the small tin hold s litres and the large tin hold b litres.
   a) Write down two equations in s and b.
   b) Solve them to find the amount each tin holds.

6. Orange juice is sold in cans and bottles. Cans hold c ml and bottles hold b ml. Three cans and four bottles contain 475 cl altogether. Four cans and three bottles hold 400 cl altogether.
   Use algebra to find how much each holds.

7. A coach journey costs each adult £a and each child £c. Tickets for one adult and two children cost £31. Tickets for two adults and three children cost £54.
   Use algebra to find the cost of each ticket.

8. The line $x + by = c$ passes through the points $(^-1, 3)$ and $(2, 9)$.
   Write down two equations and solve them to find b and c.
   Hence write down the equation of the line.

9. John's age and his father's age added together make 56. His father is 28 years older than John.
   Write these statements as equations and solve them to find their ages.

10. One boy bought 3 red lollipops and 2 green lollipops for a total of 48p. Another boy bought 2 red lollipops and 4 green lollipops for a total of 64p. Work out the cost of each lollipop.

K KEY IDEAS

- To solve linear simultaneous equations graphically, draw the lines on a graph and find where they cross.

- To solve simultaneous equations algebraically, make the coefficient of one of the letters the same in both equations. If they are the same sign, subtract the equations. If they are different signs, add the equations.

Significant figures and standard form

You will learn about

- Rounding a number to a given number of significant figures
- Using standard form to deal with large and small numbers
- Calculating with numbers in standard form

You should already know

- How to round to the nearest whole number, 10, 100, …
- How to round to a given number of decimal places
- How to round to 1 significant figure
- How to multiply and divide using the laws of indices

Rounding to a given number of significant figures

Sometimes you may be asked to give an answer to a given number of significant figures.

Significant figures are counted from left to right, starting from the first non-zero digit.

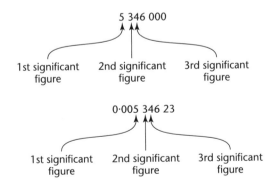

You use a similar technique to the one you use for other rounding. You look at the first digit that is not required. If this is less than 5, you round down. If it is 5 or more, you round up.

Significant figures are a good measurement of accuracy as they take the size of the number into account.

Rounding 5 346 000 to
1 significant figure   gives 5 000 000
2 significant figures   gives 5 300 000
3 significant figures   gives 5 350 000

Note that zeros are used to maintain the place value of the digits. In this case, 5 (million), 3 (hundred thousand).

Rounding 0·005 346 23 to
1 significant figure   gives 0·005
2 significant figures   gives 0·0053
3 significant figures   gives 0·005 35

Again, zeros are used to maintain the place value of the digits. In this case, 5 (thousandths), 3 (ten thousandths).

Note that zeros to the right of the first non-zero digit *are* significant. For example, 0·070 56 = 0·0706 to 3 significant figures.

EXAMPLE 1

a) Round 52 617 to 2 significant figures.

b) Round 0·072 618 to 3 significant figures.

c) Round 17 082 to 3 significant figures.

a) 52̠617 = 53 000 to 2 s.f.   To round to 2 significant figures, look at the third figure.
It is 6, so the second figure changes from 2 to 3.
Remember to add zeros for placeholders.

b) 0·072 6̠18 = 0·0726 to 3 s.f.   The first significant figure is 7.
To round to 3 significant figures, look at the fourth significant figure. It is 1, so the third figure is unchanged.

c) 17 0̠82 = 17 100 to 3 s.f.   The 0 in the middle here is a significant figure.
To round to 3 significant figures, look at the fourth figure.
It is 8, so the third figure changes from 0 to 1.
Remember to add zeros for placeholders.

EXAM TIP
Always state the accuracy of your answers when you have rounded them.

EXERCISE 11.1

1 Round each of these numbers to 1 significant figure.

a) 8·7   **b)** 9·3
c) 79·8   **d)** 0·89
e) 588   **f)** 6·502
g) 563 578   **h)** 0·076
i) 0·007 68   **j)** 0·000 348

2 Round each of these numbers to 2 significant figures.

a) 17·6   **b)** 184·2
c) 5672   **d)** 97 520
e) 50·43   **f)** 0·172
g) 0·0387   **h)** 0·006 12
i) 0·0307   **j)** 0·994

3 Round each of these numbers to 3 significant figures.

a) 8·261   **b)** 69·77
c) 16 285   **d)** 207·51
e) 12 524   **f)** 7·103
g) 50·87   **h)** 0·4162
i) 0·038 62   **j)** 3·141 59

Standard form

Standard form is a way of making very large numbers and very small numbers easy to deal with.

In standard form, numbers are written as a number between 1 and 10 multiplied by a power of 10.

Large numbers

EXAMPLE 2

Write these numbers in standard form.

a) 500 000   **b)** 6 300 000   **c)** 45 600

a) $500\,000 = 5 \times 100\,000 = 5 \times 10^5$

b) $6\,300\,000 = 6·3 \times 1\,000\,000 = 6·3 \times 10^6$

c) $45\,600 = 4·56 \times 10\,000 = 4·56 \times 10^4$

EXAM TIP

You can write down the answer without any intermediate steps.

Move the decimal point until the number is between 1 and 10.

Count the number of places the point has moved: that is the power of 10.

Significant figures and standard form

Small numbers

Write these numbers in standard form.

a) 0·000 003   **b)** 0·000 056   **c)** 0·000 726

a) $0·000\,003 = \dfrac{3}{1\,000\,000} = 3 \times \dfrac{1}{1\,000\,000} = 3 \times \dfrac{1}{10^6} = 3 \times 10^{-6}$

b) $0·000\,056 = \dfrac{5·6}{100\,000} = 5·6 \times \dfrac{1}{100\,000} = 5·6 \times \dfrac{1}{10^5} = 5·6 \times 10^{-5}$

c) $0·000\,726 = \dfrac{7·26}{10\,000} = 7·26 \times \dfrac{1}{10\,000} = 7·26 \times \dfrac{1}{10^4} = 7·26 \times 10^{-4}$

EXAM TIP

You can write down the answer without any intermediate steps.

Move the decimal point until the number is between 1 and 10.

Count the number of places the point has moved: put a minus sign in front and that is the power of 10.

CHALLENGE 1

Find the approximate distance, in kilometres, of each of the planets from the Sun.

Write the distances in standard form.

(You will find the distances in books such as atlases or encyclopaedias or on the internet.)

STAGE
8

■ EXERCISE 11.2

1 Write these numbers in standard form.
- **a)** 7000
- **b)** 84 000
- **c)** 563
- **d)** 6 500 000
- **e)** 723 000
- **f)** 27
- **g)** 53 400
- **h)** 693
- **i)** 4390
- **j)** 412 300 000
- **k)** 8 million
- **l)** 39·2 million

2 Write these numbers in standard form.
- **a)** 0·003
- **b)** 0·056
- **c)** 0·000 38
- **d)** 0·000 006 3
- **e)** 0·000 082
- **f)** 0·0060
- **g)** 0·000 000 38
- **h)** 0·78
- **i)** 0·003 69
- **j)** 0·000 658
- **k)** 0·000 000 000 56
- **l)** 0·000 007 23

3   These numbers are in standard form.
    Write them as ordinary numbers.
    a) 5×10^4 **b)** $3 \cdot 7 \times 10^5$
    c) 7×10^{-4} **d)** $6 \cdot 9 \times 10^6$
    e) $6 \cdot 1 \times 10^{-3}$ **f)** $4 \cdot 73 \times 10^4$
    g) $2 \cdot 79 \times 10^7$ **h)** $4 \cdot 83 \times 10^{-5}$
    i) $1 \cdot 03 \times 10^{-2}$ **j)** $9 \cdot 89 \times 10^8$
    k) $2 \cdot 61 \times 10^{-6}$ **l)** $3 \cdot 7 \times 10^2$
    m) $3 \cdot 69 \times 10^3$ **n)** $6 \cdot 07 \times 10^{-4}$
    o) $5 \cdot 48 \times 10^{-7}$ **p)** $1 \cdot 98 \times 10^9$

4   A billion is a thousand million.
    In 2005 the population of the world
    was 6·5 billion.
    Write the population of the world in
    standard form.

Calculating with numbers in standard form

When you need to multiply or divide numbers in standard form you can use your knowledge of the laws of indices.

EXAMPLE 4

Work out these. Give your answers in standard form.

a) $(7 \times 10^3) \times (4 \times 10^4)$

b) $(7 \times 10^7) \div (2 \times 10^{-3})$

c) $(3 \times 10^8) \div (5 \times 10^3)$

a) $(7 \times 10^3) \times (4 \times 10^4) = 7 \times 4 \times 10^3 \times 10^4$
$$= 28 \times 10^{3+4}$$
$$= 28 \times 10^7$$
$$= 2 \cdot 8 \times 10^8$$

b) $(7 \times 10^7) \div (2 \times 10^{-3}) = \dfrac{7 \times 10^7}{2 \times 10^{-3}}$
$$= 3 \cdot 5 \times 10^{7-(-3)}$$
$$= 3 \cdot 5 \times 10^{10}$$

c) $(3 \times 10^8) \div (5 \times 10^3) = \dfrac{3 \times 10^8}{5 \times 10^3}$
$$= 0 \cdot 6 \times 10^{8-3}$$
$$= 0 \cdot 6 \times 10^5$$
$$= 6 \times 10^4$$

When you need to add or subtract numbers in standard form it is much safer to change to ordinary numbers first.

EXAMPLE 5

Work out these. Give your answers in standard form.

a) $(7 \times 10^3) + (1 \cdot 4 \times 10^4)$

b) $(7 \cdot 2 \times 10^5) + (2 \cdot 5 \times 10^4)$

c) $(5 \cdot 3 \times 10^{-3}) - (4 \cdot 9 \times 10^{-4})$

a)
$$\begin{array}{r} 7\,000 \\ +\,14\,000 \\ \hline 21\,000 = 2\cdot1 \times 10^4 \end{array}$$

b)
$$\begin{array}{r} 720\,000 \\ +\,25\,000 \\ \hline 745\,000 = 7\cdot45 \times 10^5 \end{array}$$

c)
$$\begin{array}{r} 0\cdot0053 \\ -\,0\cdot00049 \\ \hline 0\cdot00481 = 4\cdot81 \times 10^{-3} \end{array}$$

Standard form on your calculator

You can do all the calculations above on your calculator using the $\boxed{\text{EXP}}$ key.

EXAMPLE 6

Find $(7 \times 10^7) \div (2 \times 10^{-3})$ using your calculator.

This is part **b)** of Example 4. These are the keys to press on your calculator.

$\boxed{7}\ \boxed{\text{EXP}}\ \boxed{7}\ \boxed{\div}\ \boxed{2}\ \boxed{\text{EXP}}\ \boxed{(-)}\ \boxed{3}\ \boxed{=}$

You should see $3 \cdot 5 \times 10^{10}$.

> ### EXAM TIP
>
> When using the $\boxed{\text{EXP}}$ key, do not enter 10 as well.
>
> On some calculators the $\boxed{(-)}$ key is marked $\boxed{+/-}$.

Sometimes your calculator will give you an ordinary number which you will have to write in standard form, if asked to give your answer in standard form. Otherwise your calculator will give you the answer in standard form.

Modern calculators usually give the correct version of standard form, for example $2 \cdot 8 \times 10^8$.

Older calculators often give a calculator version such as $2 \cdot 8^{08}$. You must write this in proper standard form, $2 \cdot 8 \times 10^8$, for your answer.

Some graphical calculators display standard form as, for example, $2 \cdot 8$ E 08.
Again you must write this in proper standard form for your answer.

Practise by checking the rest of Example 4 and Example 5 on your calculator.

EXAMPLE 7

The radius of Neptune is $2 \cdot 48 \times 10^4$ km.

Assume that Neptune is a sphere.

The surface area of a sphere is given by $4\pi r^2$.

Estimate the surface area of Neptune.

Give your answer in standard form, correct to 2 significant figures.

$A = 4\pi r^2 = 4 \times \pi \times (2 \cdot 48 \times 10^4)^2$

This is the sequence of keys to press.

$\boxed{4}$ $\boxed{\times}$ $\boxed{\text{SHIFT}}$ $\boxed{\pi}$ $\boxed{\times}$ $\boxed{(}$ $\boxed{2}$ $\boxed{\cdot}$ $\boxed{4}$ $\boxed{8}$ $\boxed{\text{EXP}}$ $\boxed{4}$ $\boxed{)}$ $\boxed{x^2}$ $\boxed{=}$

The result on your calculator should be $7\,728\,820\,583$.

So the answer is $7 \cdot 7 \times 10^9$ km^2 correct to 2 significant figures.

Checking calculations

You can also use standard form to check the order of magnitude of calculations.

EXAMPLE 8

Which of these is the correct answer to $15\,600 \times 2370$?

a) $369\,720\,000$

b) $3\,697\,200$

c) $36\,972\,000$

d) $369\,720$

Round the numbers to 1 significant figure and convert to standard form.

$15\,600$ is approximately 2×10^4.

2370 is approximately 2×10^3.

$2 \times 10^4 \times 2 \times 10^3 = 4 \times 10^7$

So **c)**, $3 \cdot 6972 \times 10^7$, is the correct answer.

STAGE

8

EXAMPLE 9

$3.89 \times 4.6 = 17.894$

Use this answer to find the answer to each of these.

a) $389\,000 \times 4600$
b) $0.000\,389 \times 0.046$
c) $3\,890\,000 \times 0.000\,046$

Round to 1 significant figure and convert to standard form.

a) $4 \times 10^5 \times 5 \times 10^3 = 20 \times 10^8$
$= 2 \times 10^9$

so the answer is $1\,789\,400\,000$.

b) $4 \times 10^{-4} \times 5 \times 10^{-2} = 20 \times 10^{-6}$
$= 2 \times 10^{-5}$

so the answer is $0.000\,017\,894$.

c) $4 \times 10^6 \times 5 \times 10^{-5} = 20 \times 10^1$
$= 2 \times 10^2$

so the answer is 178.94.

EXERCISE 11.3

Do not use your calculator for questions **1** to **5**.

1 Work out these. Give your answers in standard form.
   a) $(4 \times 10^3) \times (2 \times 10^4)$
   b) $(6 \times 10^7) \times (2 \times 10^3)$
   c) $(7 \times 10^3) \times (8 \times 10^2)$
   d) $(9 \times 10^7) \div (3 \times 10^4)$
   e) $(4 \times 10^3) \times (1.3 \times 10^4)$
   f) $(4.8 \times 10^3) \div (1.2 \times 10^{-2})$
   g) $(8 \times 10^6) \times (9 \times 10^{-2})$
   h) $(4 \times 10^8) \div (8 \times 10^2)$
   i) $(7 \times 10^{-4}) \times (8 \times 10^{-3})$
   j) $(5 \times 10^{-5}) \div (2 \times 10^4)$
   k) $(4 \times 10^3) + (6 \times 10^4)$
   l) $(7 \times 10^6) - (3 \times 10^3)$
   m) $(6.2 \times 10^5) - (3.7 \times 10^4)$
   n) $(4.2 \times 10^9) + (3.6 \times 10^8)$
   o) $(7.2 \times 10^6) - (4.2 \times 10^4)$
   p) $(7.8 \times 10^{-5}) + (6.1 \times 10^{-4})$

2 By rounding the numbers to 1 significant figure and converting to standard form, find which of these is the most likely answer to $16\,300 \times 234\,000$.
   a) $381\,420\,000$
   b) $38\,142\,000\,000$
   c) $3\,814\,200\,000$
   d) $38\,142\,000$

3 By rounding the numbers to 1 significant figure and converting to standard form, find which of these is the most likely answer to $0.000\,372 \times 0.000\,56$.
   a) $0.000\,002\,083\,2$
   b) $0.000\,000\,002\,083\,2$
   c) $0.000\,000\,208\,32$
   d) $0.000\,000\,020\,832$

EXERCISE 11.3 continued

4 $8·32 \times 5·7 = 47·424$

Using this answer and by rounding the numbers to 1 significant figure and converting to standard form, find the answer to each of these calculations.

a) $832\,000 \times 57\,000$
b) $0·000\,832 \times 0·000\,057$
c) $8320 \times 0·000\,000\,57$

5 $5·952 \div 1·92 = 3·1$

Using this answer and by rounding the numbers to 1 significant figure and converting to standard form, find the answer to each of these calculations.

a) $595\,200\,000 \div 19\,200$
b) $595\,200 \div 0·001\,92$
c) $0·000\,000\,595\,2 \div 0·000\,192$

   You may use your calculator for questions **6** to **8**.

6   Work out these. Give your answers in standard form.
a) $(6·2 \times 10^5) \times (3·8 \times 10^7)$
b) $(6·3 \times 10^7) \div (4·2 \times 10^2)$
c) $(6·67 \times 10^8) \div (4·6 \times 10^{-3})$
d) $(3·7 \times 10^{-4}) \times (2·9 \times 10^{-3})$
e) $(1·69 \times 10^8) \div (5·2 \times 10^3)$

f) $(5·8 \times 10^5) \times (3·5 \times 10^3)$
g) $(5·2 \times 10^6)^2$
h) $(3·1 \times 10^{-4})^2$
i) $(3·72 \times 10^6) - (2·8 \times 10^4)$
j) $(7·63 \times 10^5) + (3·89 \times 10^4)$
k) $(5·63 \times 10^{-3}) - (4·28 \times 10^{-4})$
l) $(6·72 \times 10^{-3}) + (2·84 \times 10^{-5})$
m) $(4·32 \times 10^{-5}) - (4·28 \times 10^{-3})$
n) $(7·28 \times 10^8) + (3·64 \times 10^6)$

7   Work out these.
Give your answers in standard form correct to 3 significant figures.
a) $(6·21 \times 10^5) \times (3·78 \times 10^7)$
b) $(8·34 \times 10^7) \div (1·78 \times 10^2)$
c) $(5·92 \times 10^8) \div (3·16 \times 10^{-3})$
d) $(6·27 \times 10^{-4}) \times (4·06 \times 10^{-3})$
e) $(9·46 \times 10^8) \div (3·63 \times 10^3)$
f) $(7·3 \times 10^4) \times (3·78 \times 10^3)$
g) $(5·63 \times 10^5)^2$
h) $(8·76 \times 10^{-4})^2$

8   The radius of Jupiter is $7·14 \times 10^4$ km.
Assume that Jupiter is a sphere.
The surface area of a sphere is given by $4\pi r^2$.
Estimate the surface area of Jupiter.
Give your answer in standard form, correct to 2 significant figures.

C CHALLENGE 2

Light takes approximately $3·3 \times 10^{-9}$ seconds to travel 1 metre.

The distance from the Earth to the Sun is $150\,000\,000$ km.

a)   Write $150\,000\,000$ km in metres using standard form.

b)   How long does it take for light to reach the Earth from the Sun?

STAGE

8

CHALLENGE 3

Paper is 0·08 mm thick.

a) Write this thickness in metres using standard form.

b) A library has $4·6 \times 10^4$ metres of shelf space.
Assuming 80% of this is filled with paper, the rest being the covers of the books,
estimate how many sheets of paper there are on the shelves.
Give your answer in standard form.

CHALLENGE 4

The hydrogen atom has a diameter of 10^{-8} cm. It has a mass of $1·7 \times 10^{-24}$ g.

a) How many atoms in a line will give a length of 1 mm?

b) How many atoms would weigh 1 kg?
Give your answer in standard form correct to 2 significant figures.

C CHALLENGE 5

The table shows some information about the Earth.

Distance from the Sun	149 503 000 km
Circumference of solar orbit	9.4×10^8 km
Speed of the Earth in solar orbit	0.106×10^6 km/h
Speed of the solar system	20·1 km/s

a) The speed of the Earth is given in index form but not in standard form.
Write the speed of the Earth in standard form.

b) How far does the Earth travel at this speed in one day?
Give your answer in standard form correct to 3 significant figures.

c) How far does the solar system travel in one day?
Give your answer in standard form correct to 3 significant figures.

d) An object travels from the Earth to the Sun and back.
How far does it travel?
Give your answer in standard form correct to 3 significant figures.

K KEY IDEAS

- 345 900 = 346 000 to 3 significant figures.

- 0·000 603 = 0·000 60 to 2 significant figures.

- Standard form is used as a way of dealing with very large and very small numbers.

- Numbers are written as $a \times 10^n$ where a is between 1 and 10 and n is an integer.

- Large numbers like 93 million (93 000 000) are written as 9.3×10^7.

- Small numbers like 0·000 007 82 are written as 7.82×10^{-6}.

- Standard form numbers are set on the calculator using the $\boxed{\text{EXP}}$ key.

- When multiplying and dividing numbers in standard form you can work out the number part and the power of 10 separately.

- You can check the order of magnitude of calculations by rounding the numbers to 1 significant figure and converting to standard form.

STAGE

8

The equation of a straight-line graph

The *gradient* of a graph is the mathematical way of measuring its steepness or rate of change.

$$\text{gradient} = \frac{\text{increase in } y}{\text{increase in } x}$$

To find the gradient of a line, mark two points on the graph, then draw in the horizontal and the vertical to form a triangle as shown.

$\text{gradient} = \frac{6}{2} = 3$

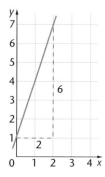

Here the gradient $= \frac{-8}{2}$ or $\frac{8}{-2}$.

Both give the answer $^-4$.

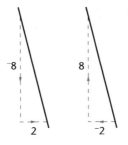

EXAM TIP

Choose two points far apart on the graph, so that the *x*-distance between them is an integer. If possible, choose points where the graph crosses gridlines. This makes reading values and dividing easier.

EXAM TIP

Check you have the correct sign, positive or negative, for the slope of the line.

Lines with a positive gradient slope forwards.

Lines with a negative gradient slope backwards.

Horizontal lines have a gradient of zero.

You can do this type of example without drawing a diagram, but do draw one if you prefer, so that you can see the triangle.

EXAMPLE 1

Find the gradient of the line joining the points (3, 5) and (8, 7).

Increase in x = 5   Subtract 8 – 3 = 5

Increase in y = 2   Subtract 7 – 5 = 2.   Remember to subtract in the same order.

Gradient = $\frac{2}{5}$ = 0·4

The equation of a straight-line graph

12

STAGE

8

When interpreting graphs about physical situations, the gradient tells you the rate of change.

EXAMPLE 2

For a distance–time graph,
the gradient gives the velocity.
Find the velocity in this graph.

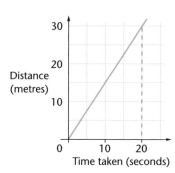

gradient $= \frac{30}{20}$ m/s $= 1.5$ m/s

velocity $= 1.5$ m/s

EXAM TIP

When calculating gradients from a graph, use the scale to work out the increase in x and y, rather than just counting the number of squares on the grid.

EXAM TIP

Use the units on the axes to help you to recognise what the rate of change represents. 'Velocity' is sometimes called 'speed'.

EXERCISE 12.1

1   Find the gradient of each of these lines.

a)

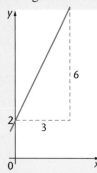

b)

c)

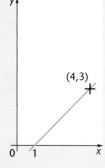

d)

e)

f)

g)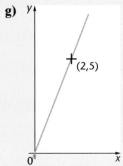

h)

i)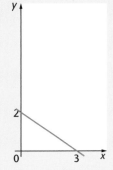

j)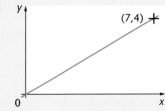

k)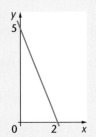

l)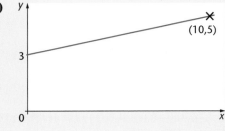

2   Calculate the gradient of the line
    joining each of these pairs of points.
    a) (3, 2) and (4, 8)
    b) (4, 0) and (6, 8)
    c) (5, 3) and (7, 3)
    d) (⁻1, 4) and (7, 2)
    e) (0, 4) and (2, ⁻6)
    f) (1, 5) and (3, 5)
    g) (⁻1, 1) and (3, 2)
    h) (⁻2, 6) and (0, 4)

3   Calculate the gradient of the line
    joining each of these pairs of points.
    a) (1, 8) and (5, 6)
    b) (2, 10) and (10, 30)
    c) (⁻3, 0) and (⁻1, 5)
    d) (⁻3, 6) and (⁻1, ⁻2)
    e) (3, ⁻1) and (⁻1, ⁻5)
    f) (0·6, 3) and (3·6, ⁻9)
    g) (2·5, 4) and (3·7, 4·9)
    h) (2·5, 7) and (4, 2·2)

4   A ball bearing rolls in a straight groove.
    The graph shows its distance from a
    point P in the groove.
    Find the gradient of the line in this
    graph. What information does it give?

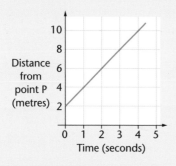

5   Find the gradient of the line in this
    graph. What information does it give?

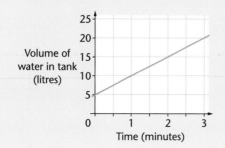

6   Find the gradient of each of the sides
    of triangle ABC.

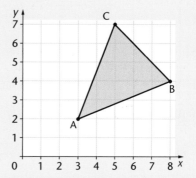

7   The table shows the cost of x minutes
    of calls on a mobile phone.

Number of minutes (x)	5	12	20	23
Cost (£C)	1·30	3·12	5·20	5·98

    Find the gradient of the graph of C
    against x, and say what this gradient
    represents.

8   The table gives the cost when x metres
    of ribbon are sold.

Number of metres (x)	0·25	0·5	1·75	3·00
Cost (C pence)	21	42	147	252

    Find the gradient of the graph of C
    against x and say what this gradient
    represents.

9   A lorry is refuelling with diesel.
    a) Draw a graph of these data.

Time (t min)	0	1	2	3
Diesel in tank (d litres)	20	30	40	50

    b) Find the gradient of the graph and
        state what it represents.

EXERCISE 12.1 continued

10 On the same diagram, draw these straight lines and find their gradients.
    a) $y = 2x$ **b)** $y = 2x + 1$
    c) $y = 3x$ **d)** $y = 3x + 2$

11 On the same diagram, draw these straight lines and find their gradients.
    a) $y = x + 1$ **b)** $y = 2x + 1$
    c) $y = 2x - 3$ **d)** $y = 5x - 2$
    e) $y = 4x$ **f)** $y = 4x + 3$

12 On the same diagram, draw these straight lines and find their gradients.
    a) $y = {}^-x + 3$ **b)** $y = {}^-2x + 1$
    c) $y = {}^-3x$ **d)** $y = {}^-3x + 2$
    e) $y = {}^-x$ **f)** $y = {}^-2x - 5$

Straight-line graphs

If you did the last three questions in the exercise on gradients, you may have noticed a connection between the equation of a line and its gradient.

ACTIVITY 1

Using graph-drawing software, draw the following lines on the same axes.
Use a different colour for each line if possible.

A $y = 2x$ $y = 2x + 1$ $y = 2x + 2$ $y = 2x + 3$ $y = 2x + 4$ $y = 2x - 1$ $y = 2x - 2$

What do you notice?
Check your ideas with these lines: $y = x$ $y = x + 1$ $y = x + 2$ $y = x + 3$

Do they work for this set?

B $y = {}^-x$ $y = {}^-x + 1$ $y = {}^-x + 2$ $y = {}^-x + 3$

Clear the screen of lines already drawn, then draw these two sets.

C $y = x$ $y = 2x$ $y = 3x$ $y = 4x$

D $y = {}^-x$ $y = {}^-2x$ $y = {}^-3x$ $y = {}^-4x$

What do you notice about the lines from **C** and **D**?
Now plot some lines of your own and see if your conclusions are correct.

STAGE

8

When the equation is written in the form $y = mx + c$, where m and c are numbers, then m is the gradient of the line and c is the value of y where the graph crosses the y-axis. In other words, the graph passes through $(0, c)$. The point $(0, c)$ is called the *y-intercept* because it is where the line intercepts, or crosses, the y-axis.

Using these facts means that, if you know the equation of a line, you can easily find its gradient and its y-intercept.

EXAMPLE 3

The equation of a straight line is $5x + 2y = 10$.
Find its gradient and y-intercept.

Rearranging the equation:
$$2y = {}^{-}5x + 10$$
$$y = {}^{-}2\cdot5x + 5$$

So the gradient is $^{-}2\cdot5$ and the y-intercept is 5.

Parallel lines

You may have noticed from the work earlier in the chapter that

Lines with the same gradient are parallel.

For example, these lines are all parallel.
$y = 2x$
$y = 2x + 3$
$y = 2x + 4$

EXAMPLE 4

State an equation for a line which is parallel to each of these.

a) $y = 4x + 1$ **b)** $y = 5 - \frac{1}{2}x$

a) The gradient of the line = 4.
Any parallel line will also have gradient 4.
So one possible line is $y = 4x - 3$.

b) The gradient of the line = $-\frac{1}{2}$.
Any parallel line will also have gradient $-\frac{1}{2}$.
So one possible line is $y = -\frac{1}{2}x + 2$ or $y = 2 - \frac{1}{2}x$.

EXERCISE 12.2

1 Find the gradient of each of these lines and their y-intercept.
   a) $y = 3x - 2$
   b) $y = 5x - 3$
   c) $y = 2 + 5x$
   d) $y = 7 + 2x$
   e) $y = 7 - 2x$
   f) $y = 9 - 3x$

2 Find the gradient of each of these lines and their y-intercept.
   a) $y + 2x = 5$
   b) $y - 5x = 1$
   c) $4x + 2y = 7$
   d) $3x + 2y = 8$
   e) $6x + 5y = 10$
   f) $2x + 5y = 15$

3 On the same diagram, sketch and label the graphs of these three equations. You do not need to do an accurate plot.
$$y = 2x + 1$$
$$y = 2x - 3$$
$$y = {}^-4x + 1$$

4 On the same diagram, sketch and label the graphs of these three equations. You do not need to do an accurate plot.
$$y = 3x + 2$$
$$y = 3x - 2$$
$$y = {}^-x + 2$$

5 Write down equations of lines parallel to each of these lines.
   a) $y = 5x$ **b)** $y = {}^-x$
   c) $y = {}^-3x + 7$ **d)** $y = 6 - 4x$
   e) $y = \frac{1}{3}x + 4$ **f)** $2y = x + 4$
   g) $2x + y = 8$ **h)** $3x + 2y = 12$
   i) $5x - 2y = 10$

C CHALLENGE 1

When a road goes up a steep slope, a road sign gives the gradient of the slope.

Investigate the different ways that gradients are given on road signs.

Is this the same on road signs in the rest of Europe?

How do these gradients relate to the mathematical gradient used in this chapter?

STAGE
8

K KEY IDEAS

■ Gradient = $\dfrac{\text{increase in } y}{\text{increase in } x}$.

■ Lines with a positive gradient slope forwards.

■ Lines with a negative gradient slope backwards.

■ Horizontal lines have a gradient of zero.

■ For graphs about physical situations, the gradient gives the rate of change.

■ Lines with the same gradient are parallel.

■ The equation of a line can be written as $y = mx + c$, where m and c are numbers; m is the gradient of the line and c is the y-intercept.

Revision exercise C1

1 Draw a grid with the *x*-axis from 0 to 10 and the *y*-axis from 0 to 7.
a) Plot the points (1, 4), (1, 6) and (2, 6) and join them to form a triangle. Label it A.
Reflect triangle A in the line $y = x$. Label the image B.
b) Rotate triangle B through 90° anticlockwise about the point (5, 5). Label the image C.
c) Describe fully the single transformation that maps triangle A on to triangle C.

2 a) Draw a grid with the *x*-axis from 0 to 12 and the *y*-axis from 0 to 6.
Plot the points (4, 1), (6, 1) and (4, 2) and join them to form a triangle. Label it D.
Translate triangle D by $\begin{pmatrix} 2 \\ 3 \end{pmatrix}$.
Label the image E.
b) Enlarge triangle E with scale factor 2 and centre of enlargement (5, 7). Label the image F.
c) Describe fully the single transformation that maps triangle D on to triangle F.

3 Draw a grid with the *x*-axis from 0 to 11 and the *y*-axis from 0 to 8.
Plot the plots A(1, 1), B(3, 1) and C(3, 2) and join them to form a triangle.
Enlarge triangle ABC by a scale factor of ‾2 with the point (4, 3) as the centre of enlargement.

4 Look at this diagram.

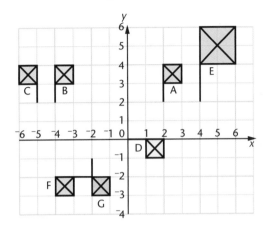

Describe fully these single transformations.
a) Flag A on to flag B
b) Flag B on to flag C
c) Flag A on to flag D
d) Flag D on to flag B
e) Flag E on to flag A
f) Flag A on to flag F
g) Flag G on to flag E

5 Solve these simultaneous equations graphically.
a) $y = x + 3$ and $y = 6 - 2x$.
Use values of *x* from ‾1 to 3.
b) $y = 2x - 1$ and $3x + 2y = 12$.
Use values of *x* from 0 to 4.

6 Solve these simultaneous equations.
a) $x + y = 15$ $2x + y = 22$
b) $2x + 3y = 13$ $3x - y = 3$
c) $2x - 3y = 3$ $4x + 5y = 17$
d) $3x - 6y = 3$ $2x + 3y = 16$
e) $x + 2y = 3$ $3x + 3y = 3$
f) $y = x + 5$ $2x + 3y = 5$
g) $2x + 3y = 8$ $5x - 2y = 1$
h) $x + y = 3$ $5x + 3y = 10$
i) $6x + 5y = \,‾2$ $4x - 3y = 5$

STAG
8

C1

7 Round each of these numbers to the number of significant figures given in brackets
   a) 78 900 (2)
   b) 0·000 538 2 (3)
   c) 635 084 (4)
   d) 0·070 385 (3)
   e) 8 496 000 (3)
   f) 0·005 03 (2)
   g) 86 749 000 (3)
   h) 0·000 997 3 (2)

8 Write these numbers in standard form.
   a) 7600   **b)** 89·9
   c) 60 000   **d)** 466
   e) 0·056   **f)** 564 600
   g) 0·0055   **h)** 67 400
   i) 0·000 042   **j)** 24 million

9 These numbers are in standard form. Write them out in full.
   a) 6×10^3 **b)** 5×10^2
   c) 7×10^{-3} **d)** $4·5 \times 10^2$
   e) $8·4 \times 10^{-3}$ **f)** $2·87 \times 10^{-3}$
   g) $4·7 \times 10^3$ **h)** $5·5 \times 10^{-2}$
   i) $7·23 \times 10^6$ **j)** $5·48 \times 10^{-5}$

10 Without using your calculator, work out these.

   Give your answers in standard form.
   a) $(3 \times 10^5) \times (2 \times 10^3)$
   b) $(4 \times 10^8) \times (1·5 \times 10^{-3})$
   c) $(8 \times 10^8) \div (2 \times 10^5)$
   d) $(6 \times 10^3) \div (2 \times 10^{-4})$
   e) $(4 \times 10^3) \times (3 \times 10^6)$
   f) $(4 \times 10^7) \div (8 \times 10^3)$
   g) $(6 \times 10^4) + (3 \times 10^3)$
   h) $(8 \times 10^5) - (3 \times 10^4)$
   i) $(6 \times 10^{-4}) + (3 \times 10^{-3})$

11 Use your calculator to work out these.

   Give your answers, in standard form, correct to 3 significant figures.
   a) $(3·2 \times 10^5) \times (2·8 \times 10^2)$
   b) $(4·6 \times 10^8) \times (1·7 \times 10^{-4})$
   c) $(8·23 \times 10^8) \div (2·6 \times 10^5)$
   d) $(6·3 \times 10^3) \div (7·9 \times 10^{-4})$
   e) $(8·9 \times 10^3) \times (6·7 \times 10^6)$
   f) $(4·53 \times 10^8) \div (8·69 \times 10^4)$
   g) $(6·3 \times 10^4) + (3·5 \times 10^3)$
   h) $(8·23 \times 10^5) - (3·78 \times 10^4)$
   i) $(6·98 \times 10^{-5}) + (3·2 \times 10^{-4})$

12 Find the gradient of the lines joining these pairs of points.
   a) (2, 4) and (4, 9)
   b) (2, 4) and (6, 0)
   c) (⁻1, 2) and (5, 2)

13 Draw a grid with the x-axis from ⁻4 to 6 and the y-axis from 0 to 7.
   Plot the points A(3, 1), B(⁻3, 4) and C(5, 6) and join them to form a triangle. Calculate the gradient of each of the sides of triangle ABC.

14 The data in the table show the distance (d km) of a car from a motorway junction at time t minutes.

t	2	4	8	15
d	5.0	7.4	12.2	20.6

   a) Draw a grid with the horizontal axis from t = 0 to 16 and the vertical axis from d = 0 to 22.
   Plot a graph to show the data in the table.
   b) What was the speed of the car, in kilometres per minute?
   c) How far was the car from the junction when t was zero?

15 Sketch the graph of each of these straight lines on a separate diagram.
   a) $y = 3x - 2$
   b) $y = {}^{-}3x + 1$
   c) $x = 2y$
   d) $x = 2$

16 For each of the lines in question **15**, write down the equation of a second line, parallel to the first.

Similar figures

You will learn about

- What similar shapes are in mathematics
- Recognising similar shapes
- Calculating lengths of sides of similar shapes

You should already know

- Angle properties of triangles and straight lines
- The angle facts for parallel lines: alternate angles, *a* and *b*, are equal and corresponding angles, *a* and *c*, are equal

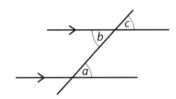

- What a scale factor is

Similar shapes

In mathematics the word 'similar' has a very exact meaning. It does *not* mean 'roughly the same' or 'alike'.

STAGE

8

For two shapes to be similar each shape must be an exact enlargement of the other. For example look at these two rectangles.

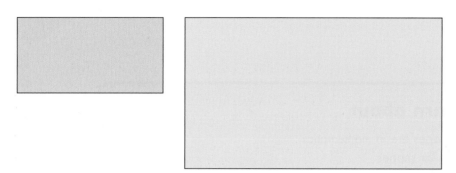

The first rectangle is 2 cm wide by 4 cm long.
The second rectangle is 4 cm wide by 7 cm long.

The rectangles are *not* similar because although the width of the large one is twice the width of the small one, the length of the large one is *not* twice the length of the small one. If the length of the large one were 8 cm then the rectangles would be similar.

Now look at these two shapes.

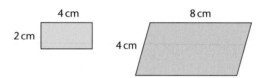

Although the scale factor for both pairs of sides is 2, the shapes are not similar because corresponding angles are not the same.

For two shapes to be similar

■ **all corresponding sides must have proportional lengths.**

■ **all corresponding angles must be equal.**

Similar triangles

ACTIVITY 1

a) Take three jointed straws. Squeeze the end of one and push it into the open end of another.
Use the third straw to join the ends of the other two to form a triangle.
Try pushing the straws to make the triangle a different shape.

b) Take four jointed straws. Join them together to form a quadrilateral.
Try pushing the straws to make the quadrilateral a different shape.

Because the lengths of three sides define a unique triangle, for two triangles to be similar only one of the tests on the previous page needs to be made.

If you can establish that the angles are the same, you can conclude that the triangles are similar and carry out calculations to find the lengths of the sides.

Calculations of lengths of similar shapes

EXAMPLE 1

The rectangles ABCD and PQRS are similar.

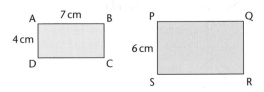

Find the length of PQ.

Since the widths of the rectangles are 6 cm and 4 cm, the scale factor is 6 ÷ 4 = 1·5.

Length of PQ = 7 × 1·5
= 10·5 cm.

STAGE

8

EXAMPLE 2

In the triangle, angle ABC = angle BDC = 90°, AB = 6 cm, BC = 8 cm and BD = 4·8 cm.

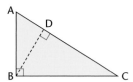

a) Explain why triangles ABC and BDC are similar.

b) Calculate the length of DC.

a) In the triangles ABC and BDC,
angle ABC = angle BDC = 90°.

The angle C is in both triangles.

Since the angle sum of a triangle
is 180°, the third angles must be equal.

So, since all the corresponding angles
are equal, the triangles are similar.

> **EXAM TIP**
> If you are asked to explain why
> two triangles are similar, look for
> reasons why the angles are equal.
> Usual reasons include 'opposite
> angles are equal', 'alternate angles
> are equal' or 'angles are in both
> triangles (common angles)'.

b) First redraw the triangles so they are the same way round as each other.

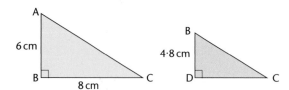

> **EXAM TIP**
> It is always easier to spot the
> corresponding sides if the shapes
> are the same way round. It is worth
> spending time redrawing the
> shapes separately and the same
> way round and marking the lengths
> on the new diagram.

Since AB = 6 cm and BD = 4·8 cm the scale factor = 4·8 ÷ 6 = 0·8.

CD = 8 × 0·8
   = 6·4 cm.

1 The two rectangles in the diagram are similar. Find the length of the larger rectangle.

2 These two parallelograms are similar. Find the length of PQ.

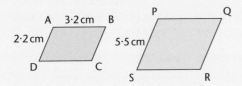

3 The triangles ABC and PQR are similar. Calculate the lengths of PQ and PR.

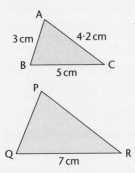

4 The triangles ABC and PQR are similar. Calculate the lengths of PQ and QR.

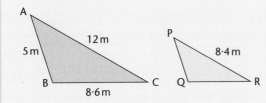

5 The triangles DEF and UVW are similar. Calculate the lengths UV and UW.

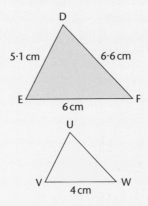

6 In the diagram, DE is parallel to BC, AB = 4·5 cm, BC = 6 cm and DE = 10 cm. Calculate the length BD.

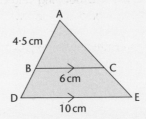

7 At noon a radio mast of height 12 m has a shadow length of 16 m. Calculate the height of a tower with a shadow length of 56 m at noon.

8 Calculate the lengths x and y in this diagram.

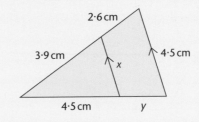

9 A stand for a small statue is made from part of a cone.
The circular top of the stand has a diameter of 12 cm; the base has a diameter of 18 cm.
The slant height of the stand is 9 cm. Calculate the slant height of the complete cone.

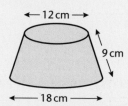

10 a) Explain how you know that the two triangles in the diagram are similar.
b) Calculate the lengths of AC and CB.

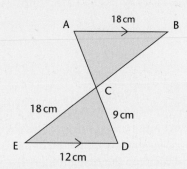

11 The line PQ is parallel to the line CD. The line QR is parallel to the line DE. Explain why the pentagons ABCDE and ABPQR are not similar.

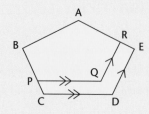

12 Explain why these quadrilaterals are *not* similar.

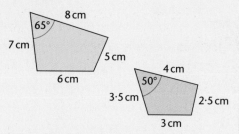

13 The lines PQ and BC are parallel.

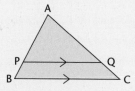

a) Explain why triangles ABC and APQ are similar.
b) If AB = 6 cm, BC = 8 cm and AP = 4·7 cm, calculate the length of PQ. Give your answer correct to 3 significant figures.

14 In the diagram, angle BAC = angle ADC = 90°, AD = 3 cm and DC = 5 cm.
a) Explain why triangles ADC and BDA are similar.
b) Calculate the length BD.

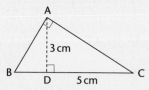

15 ABCD is a trapezium. The diagonals meet at O, and AB = 5 cm, DC = 8 cm and OD = 6 cm.
a) Explain why triangles OAB and OCD are similar.
b) Calculate the length of OB.

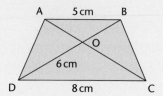

CHALLENGE 1

You need an A4 sheet of paper.

a) Measure the length and width of the paper.

b) Fold the paper in two (along the dotted line).

This size of paper is called A5.
Measure the length and width of this paper.
Divide the length of the A4 sheet by the length of the A5 piece. Do the same for the widths.
Is A4 paper similar to A5 paper? If so, what is the scale factor?

c) Fold the paper in two again. This size of paper is called A6.
Repeat part **b)** for A5 and A6 paper. What do you notice?

d) All the A-series of paper sizes work in the same way. What is the size of A3 paper?

K KEY IDEAS

- For shapes to be similar

  - all corresponding sides must have proportional lengths.

  - all corresponding angles must be equal.

- For similar triangles if one of the above conditions is true, the other must be.

STAGE

8

14 Comparing distributions

You will learn about

- Using the mean and median to compare sets of data
- Using the range and interquartile range to compare sets of data

You should already know

- How to calculate the mean, median and mode for grouped and ungrouped data
- How to calculate the range
- How to find the median and interquartile range from a cumulative frequency diagram

Comparing measures of average

If there are two (or more) sets of data, it is often necessary to make comparisons between them. For instance, if the information in the table gives the marks obtained by John and Aisha in their last five Maths tests, the question may arise as to who is better at Maths.

John	7	8	10	4	6
Aisha	8	9	7	8	6

One way to compare the two sets of figures is to calculate the mean of their scores.

John's mean = 35 ÷ 5 = 7
Aisha's mean = 38 ÷ 5 = 7·6

This would suggest that Aisha is better at Maths than John.

Whilst the mean is often a reliable way of comparing sets of data it is unwise to draw too many conclusions from such a small amount of data. It may be that the topics tested were just more suited to Aisha and, in any case, the difference is not large.

The three measurements of average, the mean, median and mode, can all be used to compare the sets of data.

Usually the mean, which takes into account all the data, is the most reliable but there are circumstances where this is not so. One or two very large or very small figures can distort a mean and give a false impression.

EXAMPLE 1

Here are John and Aisha's scores in the last ten Maths tests.

John	7	8	10	4	6	3	8	5	9	8
Aisha	8	9	7	8	6	9	8	7	6	9

Who is better at Maths?

John's mean = 68 ÷ 10 = 6·8

Aisha's mean = 77 ÷ 10 = 7·7

These figures suggest that Aisha is better at Maths and, since we now have more evidence, the conclusion is likely to be more reliable than before.

EXAMPLE 2

The tables give the sale prices of houses in two areas.
Which area has the higher house prices?

Area A		Area B	
Price in pounds (£)	Number of houses	Price in pounds (£)	Number of houses
40 000–59 999	5	40 000–59 999	0
60 000–79 999	17	60 000–79 999	16
80 000–99 999	64	80 000–99 999	27
100 000–119 999	11	100 000–119 999	47
120 000–139 999	3	120 000–139 999	10

The modal class of area A is
£80 000–£99 999.

The modal class of area B is
£100 000–£119 999.

This suggests that the houses are
more expensive in area B.

STAGE

8

EXAM TIP

When comparing measures of average, always try to interpret the information in the question. For instance, in Example 1 say that Aisha is better at Maths rather than Aisha's mean is higher than John's. In Example 2, state that the houses in area B are more expensive than those in area A, rather than that the modal class is higher.

Comparing measures of spread

When comparing sets of data, it is generally not sufficient to know that values in one set are, on average, 'bigger' than those in the other. It is also helpful to know whether one set of data is more spread out than the other.

The two measurements of spread that have been covered so far are the **range** and the **interquartile range**.

Look again at John and Aisha's scores in the last ten Maths tests.

| John | 7 | 8 | 10 | 4 | 6 | 3 | 8 | 5 | 9 | 8 |
| Aisha | 8 | 9 | 7 | 8 | 6 | 9 | 8 | 7 | 6 | 9 |

John's range is $10 - 3 = 7$.
Aisha's range is $9 - 6 = 3$.

These figures show that John's spread of scores is greater than Aisha's.

Another way of stating the conclusion is to say that Aisha is more **consistent** than John.

The range of a set of data only looks at the smallest and biggest. The data may be fairly consistent overall but have a large range. The interquartile range ignores the extreme values and so is usually a better measure with which to compare spreads.

STAGE
8

EXAMPLE 3

The cumulative frequency diagrams shown here are for the house prices in Example 2.
Compare the house prices in the two areas.

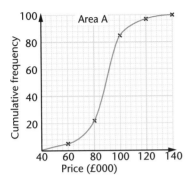

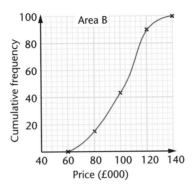

Use the diagrams to find the median and the interquartile range.

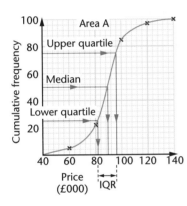

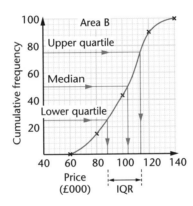

The median for area A = £89 000.
The median for area B = £104 000.
So the houses in area B are more expensive on average than those in area A.

The interquartile range for area A = £95 000 – £82 000 = £13 000.
The interquartile range for area B = £114 000 – £88 000 = £26 000.
So the spread of house prices is greater in area B than in area A.

The median, range and interquartile range of distributions can be compared visually by means of a box plot.

The box plots for the two areas look like this.

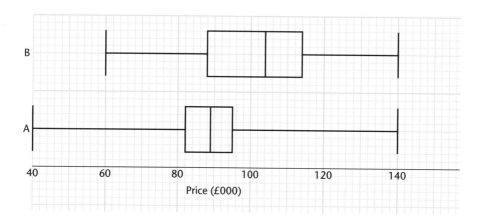

These box plots assume minimum prices of £40 000 and £60 000 and a maximum price of £139 999 for both areas, but you cannot be certain of that from the tables. In fact there is a strong likelihood that, for example, the maximum price in area A is below £139 999.

It is sometimes possible to compare spreads of distributions if there is a marked difference in the shape of the frequency diagrams.

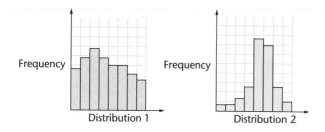

Looking at these frequency diagrams, you can see that the data in distribution 1 are much more spread out than the data in distribution 2. Or in other words the data in distribution 2 is more consistent.

EXAM TIP

When comparing the spread of data, always try to interpret the information in the question. For example, in John and Aisha's case state that Aisha is more consistent rather than that her range is smaller. In the house price question, state that area B's prices are more spread out rather than that the interquartile range is greater.

When asked to compare sets of data, always try to make both comparisons, that is relative size and spread.

EXERCISE 14.1

1 In golf the lowest score is the best. Colin's mean score in this season's golf rounds is 71. His lowest score is 63 and his highest is 88.
Vijay's mean score is 73. His lowest score is 66 and his highest score is 82. Make two comparisons of the two players' scores.

2 The median age of the Ribchester hockey team is 24 years 9 months and the range is 8 years 2 months.
The median age of the Sillington hockey team is 22 years 5 months and the range is 5 years 4 months.
Make two statements to compare the ages of the two teams.

3 The table shows the results of an investigation into costs of dental treatment in two towns.
Make two comparisons of the cost of dental treatment in the two towns.

	Median cost	Interquartile range
Town A	£19·25	£4·20
Town B	£16·50	£5·30

4 The lengths of time in minutes spent on homework by Gareth and Salima on five days in a week are listed here.

	M	Tu	W	Th	F
Gareth	50	60	45	80	70
Salima	20	80	100	30	55

Find the mean and range of the two students' times. State your conclusions.

5 Here is a set of nine numbers.

8 6 7 3 12 6 11 5 8

Write down another set of nine numbers with the same median but a larger range.

6 The table shows the mean and interquartile range of the price of a 'standard basket of shopping' in two regions of the country.
Compare the prices in the two regions.

	Mean	Interquartile range
Region A	£43·52	£3·54
Region B	£46·54	£1·68

7 The table shows the amounts of rainfall, in millimetres, in twelve months in Moralia and Sivarium.

	Moralia	Sivarium
J	25	5
F	23	6
M	21	8
A	18	12
M	18	18
J	16	78
J	15	70
A	14	21
S	18	7
O	17	4
N	22	3
D	27	2

Find the mean and range for each of the places and state your conclusions.

STAGE
8

EXERCISE 14.1 continued

8 The table shows the amounts spent on Christmas presents by the 120 students in Year 10.

Amount of money in pounds (£)	Number of students
0·00–4·99	3
5·00–9·99	14
10·00–14·99	36
15·00–19·99	50
20·00–24·99	13
25·00–29·99	4

a) Draw a cumulative frequency diagram and use it to find the median and interquartile range for the money spent.

b) The median amount spent by Year 11 students was £19, the lower quartile was £17 and the upper quartile was £21·50. The minimum was £5 and the maximum £31. Draw a box plot for each of the years.

c) Compare the distributions of money spent by Year 10 and Year 11 students.

9 Here are Tara's and Justin's marks in their last five English homeworks.

Tara	14	15	17	13	15
Justin	10	18	11	19	20

Calculate the mean and range of each of the two students' scores and state your conclusions.
Why might these conclusions be somewhat unreliable?

10 The frequency diagrams show the number of children per family, in two classes.

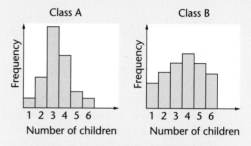

Use the modes and the shapes of the diagrams to compare the distributions.

11 The numbers of letters delivered to the houses in two roads are shown in this table.

Number of letters	Number of houses	
	Jubilee Road	Riverside Road
0	2	0
1	27	5
2	18	16
3	11	29
4	5	18
5	3	5
6	1	4
7	0	3
8	0	2
9	0	1

Find the mode and range of the numbers of letters delivered in the two roads and state your conclusions.

12 These are the weekly earnings, in pounds, of the employees at a small firm.

96 120 120 125 137 145
157 190 200 220 590

State, with reasons, which measurement of spread you would use to compare this firm with another, similar, small firm.

13 The table shows the amounts of pocket money (to the nearest pound) received by students in Class 9a.

Amount of pocket money in pounds (£)	Number of students
2	1
3	5
4	10
5	7
6	4

a) Calculate an estimate for the mean and range of the amounts of pocket money received.

b) In Class 9b the mean amount of pocket money is £3·80 and the range is £8.
Compare the amounts of pocket money in the two classes.

14 The lengths of 100 leaves from an ash tree in a park in a city centre are shown in the table.
The lengths are measured to the nearest centimetre.

Length of leaf (cm)	Frequency
9	12
10	15
11	33
12	19
13	13
14	8

a) Calculate an estimate for the mean length of leaf and estimate the range.

b) Leaves from an ash tree from a country area have a mean length of 12·7 cm and a range of 4·2 cm.
Compare the distributions of the leaves from the two different areas.

15 The cumulative frequency diagram shows the times of response to 100 alarm calls for two fire brigades.

a) Use the diagram to find the median and interquartile range of the response times for each fire brigade.

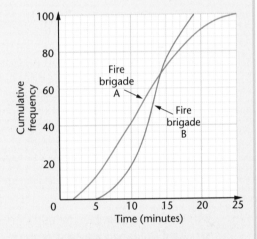

b) Comment on your results in part **a)**.
c) Draw box plots to compare the results for each fire brigade.

16 The table shows the means and interquartile ranges of two batsmen's scores in their last 20 innings.

	Mean	Interquartile range
Mike	43·4	6·4
Alec	47·8	15·2

Which batsman would you select? Explain why.

17 Panesh is buying light bulbs.
Britelite have a mean life of 300 hours with a range of 200 hours.
Lightglo have a mean life of 280 hours and a range of 20 hours.
Which type of light bulb would you advise Panesh to buy? Explain why.

18 The weekly earnings of 11 people in a small firm are listed here.
£2500   £200   £250   £350   £450   £360   £420   £375   £280   £225   £330
a) Find the median of the weekly earnings.
b) Calculate the mean of the weekly earnings.
c) Which of the answers to parts **a)** and **b)** is the fairer measurement of average?
Give your reasons.

19 A certain species of plant grows in two locations, one sheltered and the other exposed.
The two box plots below show the distribution of heights of the plants in the two
locations.

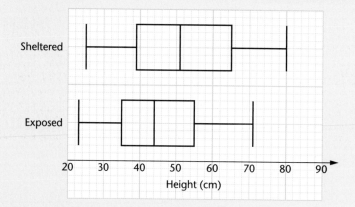

a) Which location has the taller plants? Give your reason.
b) Find the range for each of the locations.
c) Find the interquartile range for each of the locations.
d) Which of the measures you found in parts **b)** and **c)** gives the better comparison
of spread? Give your reasons.

A ACTIVITY 1

Collect some of your own data from two sources.

For example
- homework time from two year groups
- pocket money from two year groups
- amount spent on Christmas presents by girls and boys.

Compare the two sets of data using the means, medians and interquartile ranges.

You could use box plots to illustrate the data.

K KEY IDEAS

- The mean, median and mode can be used to compare the size of distributions.

- The range and interquartile range can be used to compare the spread of distributions.

- Distributions can also be compared visually using box plots.

STAGE

8

15 Trigonometry

You will learn about

- Finding length of sides and size of angles in right-angled triangles
- Solving problems using trigonometry

You should already know

- How to measure angles and make scale drawings
- How to solve simple equations
- That the longest side of a right-angled triangle is called the *hypotenuse*
- That bearings are measured clockwise from north

Labelling sides

You already know that the longest side of a right-angled triangle is called the **hypotenuse**.

The side opposite the angle you are using (θ) is called the **opposite**.

The remaining side is called the **adjacent**.

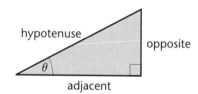

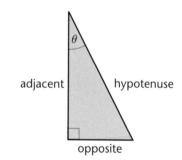

> **Hint:**
> θ is the Greek letter 'theta'.

EXAM TIP

Label the sides in the order hypotenuse, opposite, adjacent.

To identify the opposite side, go straight out from the middle of the angle. The side you hit is the opposite.

You can shorten the labels to 'H', 'O' and 'A'.

EXERCISE 15.1

Label each of the three sides in each of these triangles.

1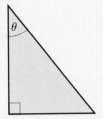

2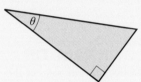

3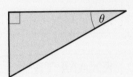

4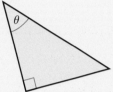

5

6

A ACTIVITY 1

- Make four drawings of this triangle.
  Draw the angles accurately but make each triangle
  a different size.

- Label the sides H, O and A appropriately.

- Measure each of the sides of all your triangles.

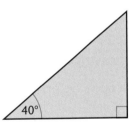

- Use your calculator to work out $\dfrac{\text{Opposite}}{\text{Hypotenuse}}$ for each triangle.

What do you notice?

Repeat the task with four right-angled triangles each containing an angle of 70°.

You should have found that your answers for each set of triangles were very close to each other. This is because all your first four triangles were similar to each other and all your second four triangles were similar to each other.

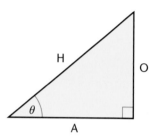

The ratio you worked out, $\dfrac{\text{Opposite}}{\text{Hypotenuse}}$, is called the **sine** of the angle.

This is often shortened to 'sin'.

$$\sin \theta = \dfrac{\textbf{Opposite}}{\textbf{Hypotenuse}}$$

> **EXAM TIP**
>
> Notice that the ratio of the lengths is written as a fraction, $\dfrac{\text{Opposite}}{\text{Hypotenuse}}$, rather than
> Opposite : Hypotenuse.

Find the $\boxed{\text{sin}}$ key on your calculator.

Find sin 40° on your calculator by pressing these keys.

$\boxed{\text{sin}}$ $\boxed{4}$ $\boxed{0}$ $\boxed{=}$

Now find sin 70°.

Check that your answers in Activity 1 are close to these answers.

> **EXAM TIP**
>
> Make sure that your calculator is set to degrees. This is the default setting but, if you see 'rad' or 'R' or 'grad' or 'G' in the window, change the setting using the $\boxed{\text{DRG}}$ key.

ACTIVITY 2

Use again the first four triangles you drew in Activity 1.

Use your calculator to work out the ratio $\dfrac{\text{Adjacent}}{\text{Hypotenuse}}$ for each triangle.

What do you notice?

Repeat this for the second group of four triangles you drew in Activity 1.

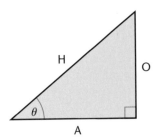

The ratio you worked out, $\dfrac{\text{Adjacent}}{\text{Hypotenuse}}$, is called the **cosine** of the angle.

This is often shortened to 'cos'.

$$\textbf{cos } \theta = \dfrac{\textbf{Adjacent}}{\textbf{Hypotenuse}}$$

Find the  key on your calculator.

Find cos 40° on your calculator by pressing these keys.

Now find cos 70°.

Check that your answers in Activity 2 are close to these answers.

A   ACTIVITY 3

Use again the first four triangles you drew in Activity 1.

Use your calculator to work out the ratio $\dfrac{\text{Opposite}}{\text{Adjacent}}$ for each triangle.

What do you notice?

Repeat this for the second group of four triangles you drew in Activity 1.

STAGE

8

The ratio you worked out, $\dfrac{\text{Opposite}}{\text{Adjacent}}$, is called the **tangent** of the angle.

This is often shortened to 'tan'.

$$\tan \theta = \dfrac{\textbf{Opposite}}{\textbf{Adjacent}}$$

Find the $\boxed{\text{tan}}$ key on your calculator.

Find tan 40° on your calculator by pressing these keys.

$\boxed{\text{tan}}$ $\boxed{4}$ $\boxed{0}$ $\boxed{=}$

Now find tan 70°.

Check that your answers in Activity 3 are close to these answers.

EXAM TIP

You need to learn the three ratios

$$\sin \theta = \frac{O}{H}, \qquad \cos \theta = \frac{A}{H} \qquad \text{and} \qquad \tan \theta = \frac{O}{A}.$$

There are various ways of remembering these but one of the most popular is to learn the 'word' '**SOHCAHTOA**'.

This stands for

S	O	H		C	A	H		T	O	A
i	p	y		o	d	y		a	p	d
n	p	p		s	j	p		n	p	j
e	o	o		i	a	o		g	o	a
	s	t		n	c	t		e	s	c
	i	e		e	e	e		n	i	e
	t	n			n	n		t	t	n
	e	u			t	u			e	t
		s				s				
		e				e				

Using the ratios 1

When you need to solve a problem using one of the ratios, you should follow these steps.

- Draw a clearly labelled diagram.
- Label the sides H, O and A.
- Decide which ratio you need to use.
- Solve the equation.

In one type of problem you will encounter you are required to find the numerator (top) of the fraction. This is demonstrated in the following examples.

EXAMPLE 1

Find the length marked x.

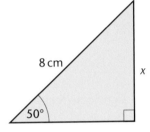

Draw a diagram and label the sides H, O and A.

Since you know the hypotenuse (H) and want to find the opposite (O), you use the sine ratio.

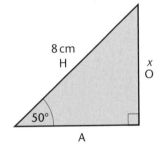

$$\sin 50° = \frac{O}{H}$$

$$\sin 50° = \frac{x}{8}$$

$8 \times \sin 50° = x$ Multiply both sides by 8.

Press these keys on your calculator to find x.

$x = 6·128\,35... = 6·13$ cm correct to 3 significant figures.

STAGE

8

EXAMPLE 2

In triangle ABC, BC = 12 cm, angle $B = 90°$ and angle $C = 35°$.
Find the length AB.

Draw the triangle and label the sides.

Since you know the adjacent (A) and want to find the
opposite (O), you use the tangent ratio.

$$\tan 35° = \frac{O}{A}$$

$$\tan 35° = \frac{x}{12}$$

$12 \times \tan 35° = x$ .... Multiply both sides by 12.

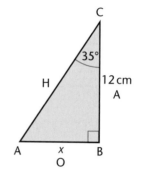

Press these keys on your calculator to find x.

| 1 | 2 | × | tan | 3 | 5 | = |

$x = 8.402\,49... = 8.40$ cm correct to 3 significant figures.

EXERCISE 15.2

1 In these diagrams find the lengths marked a, b, c, d, e, f, g and h.

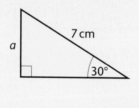

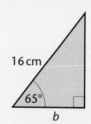

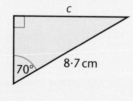

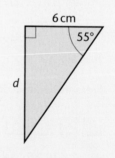

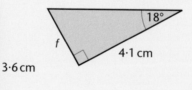

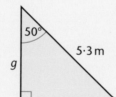

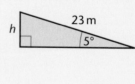

2 The ladder shown here is 6 metres long.
The angle between the ladder and the ground is 70°.
How far from the wall is the foot of the ladder?

3 **a)** Find the height, h, of the triangle.
   b) Use the height you found in part **a)** to find the area of the triangle.

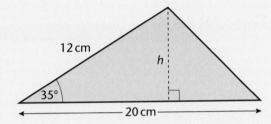

4 A ship sails on a bearing of 070° for 250 km.
   a) Find how far north the ship has travelled.
   b) Find how far east the ship has travelled.

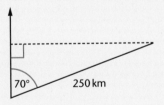

C CHALLENGE 1

The length of the crane's arm is 20 metres.

The crane can operate with the arm anywhere between 15° and 80° to the vertical.

Calculate the minimum and maximum values of x, the distance from the crane at which a load can be lowered.

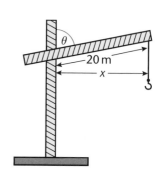

Using the ratios 2

To do the questions in this section, you need to solve equations like the ones in Example 3.

EXAMPLE 3

Find x in each of these equations.

a) $2 = \dfrac{14}{x}$ **b)** $10 = \dfrac{30}{x}$

a) $2 = \dfrac{14}{x}$

     $2x = 14$ Multiply both sides by x.

     $x = \dfrac{14}{2} = 7$ Divide both sides by 2.

b) $10 = \dfrac{30}{x}$

     $10x = 30$ Multiply both sides by x.

     $x = \dfrac{30}{10} = 3$ Divide both sides by 10.

You can use the general rule that if $a = \dfrac{b}{x}$ then $x = \dfrac{b}{a}$.

In the second type of problem you will encounter, you are required to find the denominator (bottom) of the fraction. This is demonstrated in the following examples.

EXAMPLE 4

Find the length marked x.

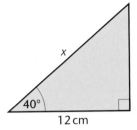

Draw the triangle and label the sides.

Since you know A and want to find H, you use the cosine ratio.

$\cos 40° = \dfrac{A}{H}$

$\cos 40° = \dfrac{12}{x}$

$x = \dfrac{12}{\cos 40°}$ Using the rule from Example 3.

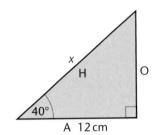

Press these keys on your calculator to find x.

$\boxed{1}\ \boxed{2}\ \boxed{÷}\ \boxed{\cos}\ \boxed{4}\ \boxed{0}\ \boxed{=}$

$x = 15.66488... = 15.7$ cm correct to 3 significant figures.

EXAMPLE 5

Find the length marked x.

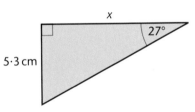

Draw the triangle and label the sides.

Since you know O and want to find A, you use the tangent ratio.

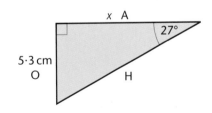

$\tan 27° = \dfrac{O}{A}$

$\tan 27° = \dfrac{5.3}{x}$

$x = \dfrac{5.3}{\tan 27°}$ Using the rule you found in Example 3.

$x = 10.40183...$ Using your calculator.

$x = 10.4$ cm correct to 3 significant figures.

> **EXAM TIP**
>
> Always look to see whether the length you are trying to find should be longer or shorter than the one you are given. If your answer is obviously wrong, you have probably multiplied instead of divided.

STAGE

8

EXERCISE 15.3

1 In these diagrams find the lengths marked *a*, *b*, *c*, *d*, *e*, *f*, *g* and *h*.

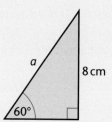

8 cm

a

60°

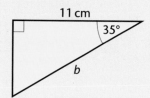

11 cm

35°

b

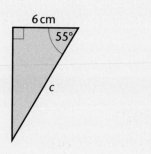

6 cm

55°

c

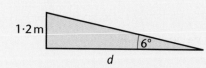

1·2 m

6°

d

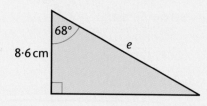

68°

8·6 cm

e

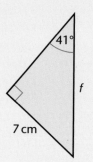

41°

f

7 cm

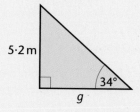

5·2 m

34°

g

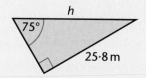

h

75°

25·8 m

2 The bearing of A from B is 040°.
A is 8 kilometres east of B.
Calculate how far A is north of B.

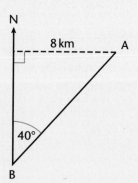

N

8 km

A

40°

B

3   The diagram shows a lean-to shed.
    a)   Find the length d.
    b)   The length of the shed is 2·5 m.
         Find the area of the roof.

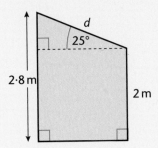

2·8 m

2 m

25°

d

4   A ship sailed on a bearing of 140°.
    It was then 90 km south of its original
    position.
    a)   Draw a diagram to show the ship's
         journey.
    b)   How far east of its original position
         is it?

C CHALLENGE 2

Mr Jones wants to buy a ladder.

His house is 5·3 metres high and he needs to reach the top.

The ladders are in two sections, each section being the same length.

When extended there must be an overlap of 1·5 metres between the two sections.

The safe operating angle is 76°.

Calculate the length of each of the sections of ladder he needs to buy.

STAGE

8

Using the ratios 3

In the third type of problem you will encounter, you are given the value of two sides and are required to find the angle. This is demonstrated in the following examples.

▌▌▌ EXAMPLE 6

Find the angle θ.

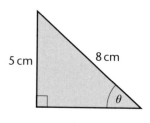

Draw the triangle and label the sides.

This time, look at the two sides you know.

Since they are O and H, you use the sine ratio.

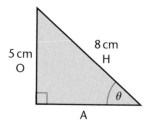

$\sin \theta = \dfrac{O}{H}$

$\sin \theta = \dfrac{5}{8}$

Work out 5 ÷ 8 = 0·625 on your calculator and leave this number in your display.

You have worked out the sine of the angle and now need to work back to the angle.

To do this, you use the sin⁻¹ function (the inverse of sin).

You will find sin⁻¹ above the │sin│ key on your calculator.

To use this function you press the key labelled SHIFT, INV or 2nd F, followed by the │sin│ key.

With 0·625 still in your display, press │SHIFT│ │sin│ │=│ , or the equivalent on your calculator.

You should see 38·682 18… .

So θ = 38·7° correct to 3 significant figures or 39° correct to the nearest degree.

Check that you do get this answer using your calculator.

You can also do the calculation in one stage by pressing these keys, or the equivalent on your calculator. Note that you *must* use the brackets.

EXAMPLE 7

Find the angle θ.

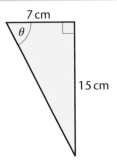

Draw the triangle and label the sides.

The two sides you know are O and A so you use the tangent ratio.

$\tan \theta = \dfrac{O}{A} = \dfrac{15}{7}$

so $\theta = \tan^{-1} \dfrac{15}{7}$

This is the sequence of keys to press on your calculator.

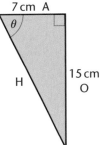

$\boxed{\text{SHIFT}}\ \boxed{\tan}\ \boxed{(}\ \boxed{1}\ \boxed{5}\ \boxed{\div}\ \boxed{7}\ \boxed{)}\ \boxed{=}$

This gives the answer θ = 64·983... = 65·0° correct to 3 significant figures.

EXAMPLE 8

Find the angle θ.

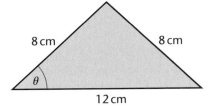

Since this is an isosceles triangle, not a right-angled triangle, you need to draw in the line of symmetry. This splits the triangle into two equal right-angled triangles.

The sides you know are A and H so you use the cosine ratio.

$\cos \theta = \dfrac{A}{H} = \dfrac{6}{8}$

so $\theta = \cos^{-1} \dfrac{6}{8}$

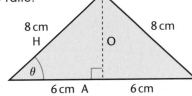

This is the sequence of keys to press on your calculator.

$\boxed{\text{SHIFT}}\ \boxed{\cos}\ \boxed{(}\ \boxed{6}\ \boxed{\div}\ \boxed{8}\ \boxed{)}\ \boxed{=}$

This gives the answer θ = 41·4° correct to 3 significant figures.

EXAM TIP

Example 8 shows how to deal with isosceles triangles. You use the line of symmetry to split the triangle into two equal right-angled triangles. This works only with isosceles triangles because they have a line of symmetry.

STAGE
8

EXERCISE 15.4

1 In these diagrams find the angles marked a, b, c, d, e, f, g and h.

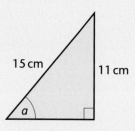

15 cm 11 cm a

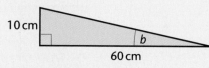

10 cm 60 cm b

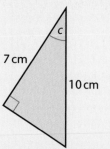

c 7 cm 10 cm

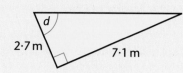

d 2·7 m 7·1 m

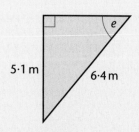

e 5·1 m 6·4 m

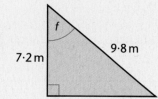

f 7·2 m 9·8 m

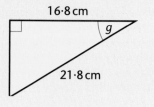

16·8 cm g 21·8 cm

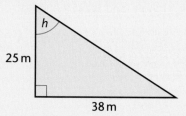

h 25 m 38 m

2 The diagram represents a ladder leaning against a wall. Find the angle the ladder makes with the horizontal.

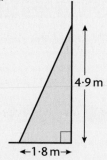

4·9 m ←1·8 m→

3 In the picture the kite is 15 metres above the girl.
The string is 25 metres long.
Find the angle the string makes with the horizontal.

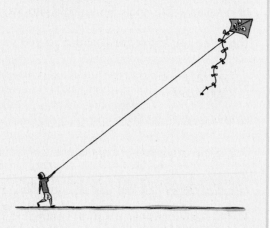

4 The diagram represents a pair of step ladders standing on a horizontal floor. Find the angle, θ, between the two parts of the step ladder.

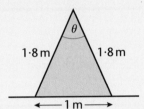

1·8 m   1·8 m

←— 1 m —→

5 An aircraft flies 180 km due east from A to B. It then flies 115 km due south from B to C.
  a) Draw a diagram to show the positions of A, B and C.
  b) Calculate the bearing of C from A.

CHALLENGE 3

A television mast is 54 metres high and stands on horizontal ground.
Six guy wires keep the mast upright.
Three of these are attached to the top and a point on the ground.
These three make an angle of 16·5° with the vertical.

a) Calculate the total length of these three wires.

b) The other three wires are attached $\frac{2}{3}$ of the way up the mast.
  They are attached to the same points on the ground as the previous three.
  Calculate the angle these make with the vertical.

KEY IDEAS

- The sides of a right-angled triangle are labelled hypotenuse, opposite and adjacent, usually abbreviated to H, O and A.

- $\sin \theta = \dfrac{O}{H}$, $\cos \theta = \dfrac{A}{H}$, $\tan \theta = \dfrac{O}{A}$.

- The steps used to solve a trigonometry problem are as follows.

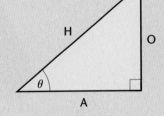

  1 Draw a clearly labelled diagram.

  2 Label the sides H, O and A.

  3 Choose which ratio you are going to use.

  4 Solve the equation.

STAGE
8

16 Dimensions

You will learn about
- Using dimensions to distinguish between formulae for length, area and volume

You should already know
- Formulae for the area of a rectangle, triangle, parallelogram, trapezium, circle
- Formulae for the volume of a cuboid, prism, cylinder

You can tell whether a formula gives a length, an area or a volume by looking at its dimensions.

A number has no dimensions.

number × length = length	(1 dimension)
length + length = length	(1 dimension)
length × length = area	(2 dimensions)
length × length × length = volume	(3 dimensions)

The area of a circle is πr^2...

...or is it $2\pi r$?

So which circle formula is for area?

Remember that π is a number and so has no dimensions.

$2\pi r$ = number × number × length
　　　 = length (the circumference of a circle)

πr^2 = number × length × length
$\quad$ = length × length
$\quad$ = area (the area of a circle)

Thinking about the number of dimensions also helps you to sort out what units you should be using. For example:

length $\;= $ m $\;$ (1 dimension)
area $\;= $ m^2 (2 dimensions)
volume $\;= $ m^3 (3 dimensions)

> **EXAM TIP**
>
> For practice, check the dimensions of formulae you know.

EXAMPLE 1

If a, b and h are lengths, does the expression $\frac{1}{2}(a + b)h$ represent a length, an area or a volume, or none of these?

$a + b$ = length

so $\frac{1}{2}(a + b)h$ = number × length × length
$\qquad\qquad = $ length × length
$\qquad\qquad = $ area

> **EXAM TIP**
>
> When adding and subtracting dimensions they must be all the same.
>
> length + length = length $\quad$ (1 dimension)
> area + area = area $\qquad\quad$ (2 dimensions)
> volume + volume = volume $\;$ (3 dimensions)
>
> Adding unlike quantities like area + length or area + volume is nonsense.

EXERCISE 16.1

Throughout this exercise, letters in algebraic expressions represent lengths.
Remember: π represents a number.

1 State whether each of these expressions represents a length, an area or a volume.
  a) $r + h$ $\qquad\qquad$ b) rh
  c) $2\pi rh$ $\qquad\qquad$ d) $a + 2b$
  e) $2ab$ $\qquad\qquad$ f) a^2b

2 Which of these expressions represent lengths?
  a) $\frac{1}{2}bh$ $\qquad\qquad$ b) $3b$
  c) $b + 2h$ $\qquad\qquad$ d) $a + 2b + c$
  e) $3a + 2a^2$ $\qquad\qquad$ f) $a(2a + b)$

3 Which of these expressions represent areas?
  a) xy $\qquad\qquad$ b) xy^2
  c) $x(x + y)$ $\qquad\qquad$ d) $4a^2$
  e) $x(x + 2y)$ $\qquad\qquad$ f) $\pi r^2 + 2\pi rh$

4 Which of these expressions represent volumes?
  a) r^3 $\qquad\qquad$ b) πr^2h
  c) $r^2(r + h)$ $\qquad\qquad$ d) πab
  e) $\frac{4}{3}\pi r^3$ $\qquad\qquad$ f) $h^2(a + b)$

STAGE

8

EXERCISE 16.1 continued

5 State whether each of these expressions represents a length, an area, a volume or none of these.

a) $r(r^2 + h)$ **b)** $(3 + \pi)h$

c) $4\pi r^2$ **d)** $\frac{1}{3}\pi r^2 h$

e) $2a^2 b(a + b)$ **f)** $a(3 + \pi)$

6 What do these formulae represent? Some of them could be nonsense.

a) $2\pi r + \pi r^2$ **b)** $2\pi rh + 2\pi r^2$

c) $\dfrac{4r^3}{3} + 2\pi rh$ **d)** $xy^2 + x^3$

e) $\frac{4}{3}\pi r^2 + 2abh$ **f)** $3xy + 5x^2$

g) $5abc + 3a^2 b$ **h)** $\frac{1}{2}bhl + r^3$

i) $\pi d + 3(a + b)$

7 Find the missing powers in these formulae.

a) Volume $= \frac{4}{3}\pi r^?$

b) Area $= \dfrac{5h^4}{3l^?}$

c) Volume $= \frac{2}{3}\pi r^3 + \pi r^? h$

A   ACTIVITY 1

Make up some formulae which would be dimensionally possible for length, area, volume and none of these.

Then swap formulae with a partner.

Work out which of your partner's formulae are for length, area, volume or none of these.

K   KEY IDEAS

- Numbers, such as 3 or π, have no dimensions.

- To check a formula look at the dimensions. Length × length always gives area. Length × length × length always gives volume.

Revision exercise D1

1 The two rectangles are similar. Calculate the height of the smaller rectangle.

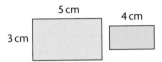

2 Are these rectangles similar? Show a calculation to explain your answer.

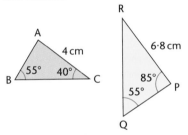

3 a) Explain why triangles ABC and PQR are similar.

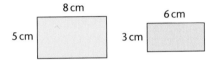

   b) What is the scale factor?

4 Triangle PQR is similar to triangle ABC. Calculate the lengths PR and QR.

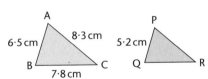

5 Over the last month, David's mean journey time to work was 43 minutes, with an interquartile range of 7 minutes.
Angie's mean time was 32 minutes, with an interquartile range of 12 minutes.
Make two comparisons of David's and Angie's journey times.

6 Eleven members of Class 10G and eleven members of Class 10F were given a Maths problem to solve.
The times, in seconds, they took to solve the problem are shown in the table.

Class 10F	Class 10G
17	4
15	13
11	15
9	11
6	32
27	7
18	9
21	12
6	6
19	10
8	14

Find the median and range for each class and comment on the results.
Why might the interquartile range be a better measurement to use?

7 A survey was carried out on 50 adults in each of England and France to study the amount of wine consumed in a year.
The table shows the mean and interquartile range of the number of bottles consumed in each of the countries.

	Mean	Interquartile range
England	21	9
France	46	8

Compare the two countries.

8 The table shows the prices of a sample of 100 houses in the Northwest of England.

Price (£000)	Number of houses
$80 < x \leqslant 100$	2
$100 < x \leqslant 120$	4
$120 < x \leqslant 140$	13
$140 < x \leqslant 160$	26
$160 < x \leqslant 180$	37
$180 < x \leqslant 200$	10
$200 < x \leqslant 220$	5
$220 < x \leqslant 240$	3

a) Use mid-interval values of £90 000, £110 000, £130 000, £150 000, £170 000, £190 000, £210 000 and £230 000 to estimate the mean house price in the sample.

b) A similar sample in the Southeast gave a mean of £207 000 and a range of £210 000. Compare the two areas.

9 Calculate the lengths and angles marked with letters. (All lengths are in centimetres.)

a)
23, 40, a

b)
8, 7, a

c)
7, a, 12

d)
14, x, 37°

e)
9, 50°, x

f)
48°, 13, x

10 A boy is flying a kite with a string of length 45 m.
The string is straight and it makes an angle of 75° with the ground.
How high is the kite? (Ignore the height of the boy.)

11 The sides of a triangle are 5 cm, 5 cm and 7 cm.
Calculate the angles of the triangle.

12 A ramp for disabled people must slope at not more than 10° to the horizontal.
The height of the ramp is 0·8 m.
How long is the ramp?

0·8 m
10°

13 A man sails for 5 km on a bearing of 285° from a harbour.
a) How far north and west of the harbour is he?
He then sails 3 km due north.
b) Find the bearing on which he needs to sail to return to the harbour, and how far he needs to sail.

14 In these expressions, r and h are lengths. State which of length, area and volume is represented by each of these expressions.
a) $\pi r h + \pi r^2$
b) $\frac{1}{2}(r + h)$
c) $3r^2 h$

15 Find the missing powers in these formulae.
a) volume $= \frac{1}{3}\pi r^? h$
b) area $= 6r^?$
c) length $= \dfrac{r^?}{h^2}$

You will learn about

- Multiplying out pairs of brackets
- Factorising expressions of the form $x^2 + ax + b$
- Factorising expressions of the form $x^2 - a^2$

You should already know

- How to collect together simple algebraic terms
- How to expand single brackets
- How to take out common factors

Multiplying out two brackets

You may have learnt how to multiply out pairs of brackets in Stage 7 but it is such an important topic in algebra that it is repeated here.

The following examples show two different methods of organising your work to make sure you do not forget any of the four terms.

The different methods produce exactly the same four terms which are simplified to obtain the answers.

EXAM TIP

Apart from multiplying out the brackets, you may sometimes be asked to simplify, expand or remove the brackets, which all mean the same thing.

STAGE
8

EXAMPLE 1

Expand these.

a) $(x + 6)(x + 2)$ **b)** $(x + 5)(x - 2)$ **c)** $(x - 3)(x - 2)$

a) Method 1

Use a grid to multiply each of the terms in the second bracket by each of the terms in the first bracket.

$\times$	x	$^{+}6$
x	x^2	$^{+}6x$
$^{+}2$	$^{+}2x$	$^{+}12$

$= x^2 + 6x + 2x + 12$
$= x^2 + 8x + 12$

> **Hint:**
> You should always collect like terms together:
> $6x + 2x = 8x$.

Method 2

Use the word FOIL to make sure you multiply each term in the second bracket by each term in the first.

F: first $\times$ first
O: outer $\times$ outer
I: inner $\times$ inner
L: last $\times$ last

If you draw arrows to show the multiplications, you can think of a smiley face.

$(x + 6)(x + 2)$

$= x \times x + x \times 2 + 6 \times x + 6 \times 2$
$= x^2 + 2x + 6x + 12$
$= x^2 + 8x + 12$

> **EXAM TIP**
> Choose the method you prefer and stick to it.

b) Method 1

$\times$	x	$^{+}5$
x	x^2	$^{+}5x$
$^{-}2$	$^{-}2x$	$^{-}10$

$= x^2 + 5x - 2x - 10$
$= x^2 + 3x - 10$

▌EXAMPLE 1 continued

Method 2

$= x \times x + x \times (^-2) + 5 \times x + 5 \times (^-2)$
$= x^2 - 2x + 5x - 10$
$= x^2 + 3x - 10$

c) Method 1

×	**x**	**⁻3**
x	x^2	^-3x
⁻2	^-2x	$^+6$

$= x^2 - 3x - 2x + 6$
$= x^2 - 5x + 6$

Method 2

$= x \times x + x \times (^-2) + (^-3) \times x + (^-3) \times (^-2)$
$= x^2 - 2x - 3x + 6$
$= x^2 - 5x + 6$

> **EXAM TIP**
>
> Most errors are made in multiplying out the second bracket when the sign in front is negative.

There are two other types of expansions of two brackets that you need to know.

The first is when a bracket is squared, as in parts **a)** and **b)** of Example 2. The important thing with this type of expansion is to make sure that you write the brackets separately and that you end up with three terms.

The second type is shown in part **c)** of Example 2. With this type of expansion, you get only two terms because the middle terms cancel each other out. This type is known as the **difference of two squares** because $(A - B)(A + B) = A^2 - B^2$.

EXAMPLE 2

Expand these brackets.

a) $(a + 4)^2$ **b)** $(a - 4)^2$ **c)** $(a + 4)(a - 4)$

a) $(a + 4)^2 = (a + 4)(a + 4)$
$= a^2 + 4a + 4a + 16$ Using either method.
$= a^2 + 8a + 16$

b) $(a - 4)^2 = (a - 4)(a - 4)$
$= a^2 - 4a - 4a + 16$ Using either method.
$= a^2 - 8a + 16$

EXAM TIP
Take care with the negative signs.

c) $(a + 4)(a - 4) = a^2 - 4a + 4a - 16$ Using either method.
$= a^2 - 16$

EXAM TIP
The important thing in Example 2 parts **a)** and **b)** is to make sure that you write the brackets separately and that you end up with three terms.

EXAM TIP
Some people can multiply out two brackets without writing down anything. However, you are more likely to make an error by missing steps and so it is worth showing every step in an examination.

EXERCISE 17.1

Multiply out the brackets.

1 $(a + 2)(a + 4)$ **11** $(a - 1)(a - 2)$

2 $(a + 5)(a + 1)$ **12** $(a - 5)(a + 3)$

3 $(x + 6)(x + 1)$ **13** $(x - 2)(x + 3)$

4 $(x + 2)(x + 9)$ **14** $(y - 5)(y + 4)$

5 $(a + 7)(a + 3)$ **15** $(x - 8)(x - 2)$

6 $(a + 3)(a + 10)$ **16** $(a - 9)(a - 2)$

7 $(y + 3)(y - 5)$ **17** $(y + 5)^2$

8 $(x - 7)(x + 4)$ **18** $(x + 11)(x - 2)$

9 $(a + 2)(a - 6)$ **19** $(x - 1)^2$

10 $(p + 6)(p - 3)$ **20** $(x - 3)^2$

21 $(y + 2)^2$

22 $(y - 2)^2$

23 $(a - 6)^2$

24 $(a + 6)^2$

25 $(a + 8)^2$

26 $(x + 3)(x - 3)$

27 $(x + 5)(x - 5)$

28 $(a + 8)(a - 8)$

29 $(a + 9)(a - 9)$

30 $(a + 20)^2$

31 $(y - 1)(y + 1)$

32 $(a + 6)(x - 6)$

33 For this diagram write down the length and width and then multiply them to find the total area.

C **CHALLENGE 1**

You can use the same methods to multiply out harder brackets. For example

$(5a - 2b)(3a - 2b) = 15a^2 - 10ab - 6ab + 4b^2$ Using either method.
$= 15a^2 - 16ab + 4b^2$

Now try these.

a) $(x - 2)(2x + 1)$

b) $(4a - b)(a + 2b)$

c) $(4 - 3b)(5 + 2b)$

d) $(4x - 3y)^2$

e) $(3a + b)(3a - b)$

f) $(4a - 3b)(2a - 3b)$

Note that part **e)** is another example of 'difference of two squares'.

STAGE

8

Quadratics

C CHALLENGE 2

For this diagram, write down the length and width and then multiply them to find the total area.

$2x$ 3

x

2

Factorising expressions of the form $x^2 + ax + b$

A ACTIVITY 1

Copy and multiply out these brackets. See if you can discover a relationship between the numbers in the brackets and the numbers in the final expression.

$(x + 1)(x + 2) = x^2 + 3x + 2$

$(x + 1)(x + 3) =$

$(x + 1)(x + 4) =$

$(x + 2)(x + 3) =$

$(x + 2)(x + 4) =$

Do more if you need to.

Do your rules work for negative numbers?

Try $(x - 1)(x - 2) =$

$(x - 1)(x - 3) =$

STAGE

8

Expressions where the last sign is positive

You found in Example 1 that the expression $(x + 6)(x + 2)$ can be multiplied out and simplified to give $x^2 + 8x + 12$.

Therefore $x^2 + 8x + 12$ can be factorised as a product of two brackets, by reversing the process.

The order in which you write the brackets does not matter.

EXAMPLE 3

Factorise $x^2 + 7x + 12$.

This will factorise into two brackets with x as the first term in each.

$x^2 + 7x + 12 = (x \quad)(x \quad)$

As both the signs are positive, both the numbers will be positive.

Using the result from Activity 1, you need to find two numbers that multiply to give 12 and add to give 7.

These are $^+3$ and $^+4$.

So $x^2 + 7x + 12 = (x + 3)(x + 4)$ or $x^2 + 7x + 12 = (x + 4)(x + 3)$.

EXAM TIP

If the last sign is positive (+), both the signs in the brackets must be the same as the sign before the x-term.

If the middle sign is negative and the last sign is positive, or vice versa, the two numbers will be negative.

EXAMPLE 4

Factorise $x^2 - 3x + 2$.

You need to find two negative numbers that multiply to give $^+2$ and add to $^-3$. They are $^-2$ and $^-1$.

$x^2 - 3x + 2 = (x - 2)(x - 1)$.

A ACTIVITY 2

Some of these factors are correct and some are wrong. Can you find which?

a) $x^2 + 16x + 15 = (x + 5)(x + 3)$

b) $p^2 - 9p + 8 = (p - 1)(p - 8)$

c) $a^2 - 7a + 12 = (a - 4)(a - 3)$

d) $x^2 - 13x + 36 = (x + 4)(x + 9)$

Correct the wrong ones.

STAGE
8

Quadratics

EXERCISE 17.2

Factorise these expressions.

1	$x^2 + 5x + 6$	**16**	$a^2 - 2a + 1$
2	$x^2 + 7x + 10$	**17**	$y^2 - 9y + 14$
3	$x^2 + 6x + 5$	**18**	$b^2 - 10b + 24$
4	$x^2 + 4x + 3$	**19**	$x^2 - 6x + 8$
5	$x^2 + 6x + 8$	**20**	$c^2 - 4c + 3$
6	$x^2 + 8x + 15$	**21**	$a^2 + 8a + 12$
7	$x^2 + 5x + 4$	**22**	$a^2 + 15a + 36$
8	$x^2 + 9x + 20$	**23**	$a^2 - 6a + 9$
9	$x^2 + 2x + 1$	**24**	$x^2 - 12x + 27$
10	$x^2 + 7x + 6$	**25**	$b^2 - 12b + 32$
11	$x^2 - 7x + 6$	**26**	$b^2 - 10b + 25$
12	$x^2 - 9x + 18$	**27**	$x^2 + 11x + 24$
13	$x^2 - 7x + 10$	**28**	$x^2 + 14x + 24$
14	$x^2 - 7x + 12$	**29**	$x^2 - 9x + 20$
15	$x^2 - 4x + 3$	**30**	$x^2 - 15x + 56$

Expressions where the last sign is negative

EXAMPLE 5

Factorise $x^2 - 3x - 10$.

As the last sign is negative, you need two numbers, with opposite signs, that multiply to give ⁻10 and add to give ⁻3. The numbers are ⁻5 and ⁺2.

$x^2 - 3x - 10 = (x - 5)(x + 2)$

EXAMPLE 6

Factorise $x^2 + 4x - 12$.

The last sign is negative, so you need two numbers, with opposite signs, that multiply to give $^-12$ and add to give $^+4$. The numbers are $^+6$ and $^-2$.

$x^2 + 4x - 12 = (x + 6)(x - 2)$

EXERCISE 17.3

Factorise these expressions.

1 $x^2 - 2x - 8$

2 $x^2 + 2x - 3$

3 $x^2 + 4x - 5$

4 $x^2 + 3x - 10$

5 $x^2 - x - 6$

6 $x^2 - x - 12$

7 $x^2 + 5x - 6$

8 $x^2 + 5x - 14$

9 $x^2 + 2x - 3$

10 $x^2 - 2x - 15$

11 $x^2 - 3x - 18$

12 $x^2 - 3x - 28$

13 $x^2 - 9x - 10$

14 $x^2 - 17x + 30$

15 $x^2 + 9x + 14$

16 $x^2 + 4x - 32$

17 $y^2 + 9y - 22$

18 $a^2 + 9a - 36$

19 $x^2 + x - 12$

20 $x^2 + x - 20$

21 $a^2 + 8a - 20$

22 $y^2 + 19y + 48$

23 $a^2 - 6a - 27$

24 $a^2 - 6a - 16$

25 $b^2 + 12b + 20$

26 $b^2 - 15b + 36$

27 $x^2 + 11x - 26$

28 $x^2 + 7x - 30$

29 $x^2 - 9x + 18$

30 $x^2 - 3x - 40$

EXAM TIP

Remember that if the last sign is negative the two numbers have different signs and the larger number has the sign of the x-term.

It is easy to make a mistake when factorising. Always check by multiplying out the brackets.

Factorising expressions of the form $x^2 - b^2$

Multiplying out $(x - 4)(x + 4)$ gives $x^2 + 4x - 4x - 16$. This is $x^2 - 16$ when simplified. The x-terms disappear.

Similarly, $(x - 3)(x + 3) = x^2 - 9$.

So, following this pattern we see that

$x^2 - b^2$ **factorises to** $(x - b)(x + b)$.

> **EXAM TIP**
> It is worth learning this so that you recognise it when you see it!

EXERCISE 17.4

Factorise these expressions.

1 $x^2 - 4$

2 $x^2 - 1$

3 $x^2 - 25$

4 $x^2 - 36$

5 $x^2 - 49$

6 $x^2 - 81$

7 $y^2 - 100$

8 $m^2 - 144$

9 $y^2 - 400$

10 $a^2 - 169$

11 $y^2 - 121$

12 $b^2 - 225$

13 $a^2 - 289$

14 $p^2 - q^2$

C CHALLENGE 3

You can sometimes factorise quadratic expressions by spotting a common factor. You take this common factor out first and then factorise the remainder.

Factorise these by taking out a common factor first.

a) $2x^2 + 6x + 4$

b) $3x^2 - 21x + 30$

c) $2x^2 + 4x - 16$

d) $5x^2 - 45$

CHALLENGE 4

Work in pairs.

Write your own quadratic expression (either one that will factorise or one that will not).

Challenge your partner to say if it factorises or not, and to carry out the factorisation if it does.

If they are correct, they score one point, if they are wrong they score nothing.

The first to score five points wins.

 KEY IDEAS

- When multiplying two brackets, multiply every term in the first bracket by every term in the second bracket.

- To factorise $x^2 + ax + b$:
  If b is positive, find two numbers that multiply to give b and add up to a.
  If b is negative, find two numbers that multiply to give b and have a difference of a.

- The difference of two squares, $x^2 - a^2$, factorises as $(x + a)(x - a)$.

STAGE

8

Time series and moving averages

Time series

The table below shows the value, in thousands of pounds, of an ice-cream company's quarterly sales for 2002 to 2005.

	1st quarter	2nd quarter	3rd quarter	4th quarter
2002	145	256	328	258
2003	189	244	365	262
2004	190	266	359	250
2005	201	259	401	265

The graph illustrates these figures.

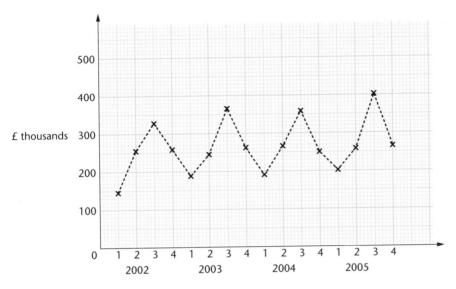

Note that the points have been joined by broken lines. Points on graphs should, really, only be joined when it makes sense to read off in between the points. Here, since the figures are total sales it does not make sense to do so. Often, however, it is useful to join the points with broken lines to show the trend.

The figures and graph are an example of a time series. You can see that there are 'peaks' at each 3rd quarter and 'troughs' at each 1st quarter. When you have a repeating pattern or 'cyclical' effect like this it is sometimes difficult to see trends.

Other examples of figures which may be 'cyclical' are monthly or seasonal rainfall or monthly or seasonal unemployment figures in certain areas.

Moving averages

Moving averages give you a way of seeing trends in figures that are 'cyclical'. They are calculated as shown below.

Look at the figures for the first four quarters above.

The mean = $(145 + 256 + 328 + 258) \div 4 = 246 \cdot 75$.

Then find the mean for the second group of consecutive quarters, that is $(256 + 328 + 258 + 189) \div 4 = 257 \cdot 75$.

Notice that 2002 quarter 1 is omitted and 2003 quarter 1 is included.

Now find the next mean by omitting the 256 and including the next quarter, 244, that is $(328 + 258 + 189 + 244) \div 4 = 254 \cdot 75$.

The next mean is $(258 + 189 + 244 + 365) \div 4 = 264$.

This is continued until the last quarter is included, each time omitting the first figure and 'picking up' the next one in the table.

If all the quarters' figures are put in order and numbered as below, the lines underneath move along one each time and indicate the numbers which should be used.

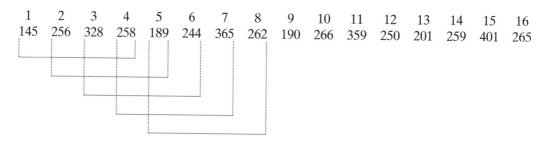

and so on.

Check that you agree with this complete list.

Quarters	Moving average
1–4	246·75
2–5	257·75
3–6	254·75
4–7	264
5–8	265
6–9	265·25
7–10	270·75
8–11	269·25
9–12	266·25
10–13	269
11–14	267·25
12–15	277·75
13–16	281·5

STAGE

8

These points are now plotted on the graph. They are plotted at the middle of the intervals of points. That is at 2·5 for quarters 1 to 4, at 3·5 for the next four quarters and so on.

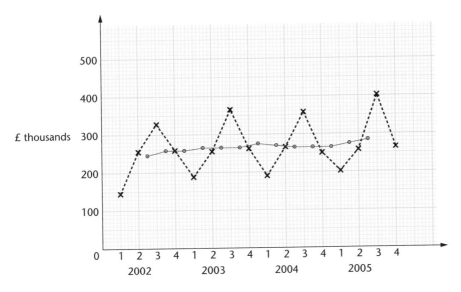

You can see that plotting the moving averages flattens out the peaks and troughs and shows a fairly flat graph with possibly a slight overall increase.

When four figures are used to find a moving average, as is the case in quarterly figures, then this is called a 'four-quarter (or four-point) moving average'.

A ACTIVITY 1

Discuss situations when it might be suitable to use each of these.

a) seven-point moving average

b) four-point moving average

c) twelve-point moving average

d) five-point moving average

STAGE
8

EXAMPLE 1

This graph shows the number of units of electricity used each quarter by the Peters' family over 5 years, together with the four-point moving averages.

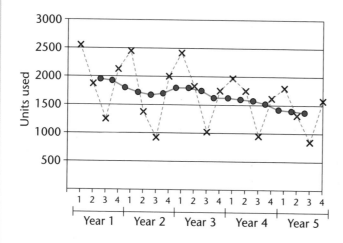

a) Describe the seasonal variation.

b) Describe the long-term trend.

a) Each year, the greatest use of electricity by the Peters' family is in the first quarter (winter) with the least use being in the third quarter (summer).

b) The general trend is for reduced use of electricity.

EXERCISE 18.1

1   The table shows the gross Accident & Health Insurance premiums paid in the Netherlands for the four quarters of 2004 to 2006. The figures are in millions of euros.

	1st quarter	2nd quarter	3rd quarter	4th quarter
2004	43	17	15	15
2005	47	19	18	18
2006	57	26	22	13

a) Plot these figures in a graph. Use a scale of 1 cm to each quarter on the horizontal axis and 2 cm to 10 million euros on the vertical axis.

b) Calculate the four-quarter moving averages.

c) Plot the moving averages on your graph.

d) Comment on the general trend and the quarterly variation.

2 The table shows a household's quarterly expenditure on fuel and light in the years 2002 to 2005. The figures are in pounds.

	1st quarter	2nd quarter	3rd quarter	4th quarter
2002	380	272	264	371
2003	432	285	207	272
2004	298	192	158	285
2005	310	208	182	291

a) Plot these figures in a graph. Use a scale of 1 cm to each quarter on the horizontal axis and 2 cm to 100 pounds on the vertical axis.

b) Calculate the four-quarter moving averages.

c) Plot the moving averages on your graph.

d) Comment on the general trend and the quarterly variation.

e) During this period, major insulation work was carried out on the house. When do you think that was?

3 The table shows the total sales in megawatts from Danish wind turbines in the years 2002 to 2005.

	1st quarter	2nd quarter	3rd quarter	4th quarter
2002	96·6	125·8	122·9	229·1
2003	74·1	143·1	173·0	335·9
2004	216·2	234·2	234·5	282·6
2005	168·8	239·7	282·1	525·4

a) Plot these figures in a graph. Use a scale of 1 cm to each quarter on the horizontal axis and 2 cm to 100 megawatts on the vertical axis.

b) Calculate the four-quarter moving averages.

c) Plot the moving averages on your graph.

d) Comment on the general trend and the quarterly variation.

4   The table shows the number of bankruptcies in Auckland by quarters from 2002
    to 2005.

	1st quarter	2nd quarter	3rd quarter	4th quarter
2002	60	61	72	57
2003	83	75	90	66
2004	62	96	99	79
2005	72	63	79	65

a) Plot these figures in a graph. Use a scale of 1 cm to each quarter on the horizontal
    axis and 2 cm to 20 bankruptcies on the vertical axis.
b) Calculate the four-quarter moving averages.
c) Plot the moving averages on your graph.
d) Comment on the general trend and the quarterly variation.

5   The table shows a company's quarterly sales of raincoats in the years 2003 to 2006.
    The figures are in thousands of pounds.

	1st quarter	2nd quarter	3rd quarter	4th quarter
2003	154	121	63	134
2004	132	106	72	108
2005	115	111	58	97
2006	110	93	47	82

a) Plot these figures in a graph. Use a scale of 1 cm to each quarter on the horizontal
    axis and 2 cm to 20 thousand pounds on the vertical axis.
b) Calculate the four-quarter moving averages.
c) Plot the moving averages on your graph.
d) Comment on the general trend and the quarterly variation.

EXERCISE 18.1 continued

6 The table shows the daily sales of a shop over a three-week period. The figures are in thousands of pounds.

	Monday	Tuesday	Wednesday	Thursday	Friday	Saturday	Sunday
Week 1	7·3	8·8	9·2	10·3	15·5	16·2	12·8
Week 2	6·7	7·8	10·1	11·8	14·7	17·9	11·3
Week 3	7·1	6·3	8·2	10·9	12·9	16·6	11·6

   a) Plot these figures in a graph. Use a scale of 1 cm to each day on the horizontal axis and 2 cm to 2 thousand pounds on the vertical axis.
   b) Calculate the seven-day moving averages.
   c) Plot the moving averages on your graph.
   d) Comment on the general trend and the daily variation.

7 The table shows the daily audiences for a four-week Christmas pantomime season.

	Monday	Tuesday	Wednesday	Thursday	Friday	Saturday
Week 1	256	312	324	452	600	580
Week 2	297	367	382	538	600	600
Week 3	248	327	325	495	570	583
Week 4	192	219	287	306	490	572

   a) Plot these figures in a graph. Use a scale of 1 cm to each day on the horizontal axis and 2 cm to 100 people on the vertical axis.
   b) Calculate the six-day moving averages.
   c) Plot the moving averages on your graph.
   d) Comment on the general trend and the daily variation.

EXERCISE 18.1 continued

8 The table shows the monthly number of US citizens flying to Europe from 2004 to 2006. The figures are in 100 thousands.

	Jan	Feb	Mar	Apr	May	Jun	Jul	Aug	Sep	Oct	Nov	Dec
2004	5·8	5·4	7·6	7·5	10·3	11·8	10·9	9·9	10·2	8·0	6·8	7·0
2005	6·3	5·9	8·9	8·5	11·0	12·8	12·0	10·3	10·8	8·8	7·1	7·4
2006	6·4	6·2	10·3	9·3	11·5	13·2	12·5	11·0	11·1	9·4	8·2	7·5

   a) Plot these figures in a graph. Use a scale of 1 cm to two months on the horizontal axis and 1 cm to 100 000 thousand citizens on the vertical axis.
   b) Calculate the twelve-month moving averages.
   c) Plot the moving averages on your graph.
   d) Comment on the general trend and the monthly variation.

9 The table shows the number of people visiting a doctors' surgery each day for a four-week period.

	M	Tu	W	Th	F
Week 1	105	71	63	84	92
Week 2	126	86	71	94	115
Week 3	142	91	84	88	104
Week 4	115	82	73	84	91

   a) Plot a time-series graph of these figures.
   b) Calculate the five-day moving averages and add these to the graph.
   c) Describe the trend over this period.

STAGE
8

10 The graph shows a shop's quarterly sales of rainwear.

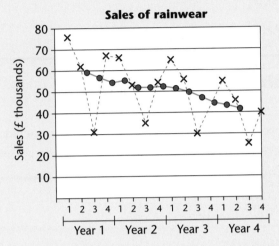

Sales of rainwear

a) Use readings from this graph to show how the fifth moving average has been calculated.

b) Comment on the seasonal variation and trends shown on the graph.

KEY IDEAS

- A time series shows the variation of sets of figures over periods of time. These periods can be quarterly, daily, monthly and so on. These are usually displayed on a graph.

- Moving averages are used to help 'iron out' the variation and to enable any long-term trends to be identified more easily.

- To calculate a moving average, for example for quarterly figures, first calculate the mean for the first four quarters. Then omit the first quarter and include the fifth quarter and find the new mean. Then omit the second quarter and include the sixth and so on.

- The moving averages are plotted at the middle of the interval.

STAGE

8

Equations and formulae

You will learn about

- Solving quadratic equations using factorisation
- Rearranging formulae and equations where the subject occurs more than once or is raised to a power

You should already know

- How to factorise quadratic expressions of the form $x^2 + ax + b$, $x^2 + ax$ and $x^2 - a^2$
- How to rearrange simple formulae

Solving quadratic equations

ACTIVITY 1

Try to find two numbers which multiply together to give zero.

For any two numbers, if $A \times B = 0$, then either $A = 0$ or $B = 0$.

If $(x - 3)(x - 2) = 0$ then either $(x - 3) = 0$ or $(x - 2) = 0$.

To solve a quadratic equation, factorise it into two brackets and then use this fact.

Remember, to factorise $x^2 + ax + b$,
- if b is positive, find two numbers with product b and sum a; the signs in the bracket are both the same as a.
- if b is negative, find two numbers with product b and difference a; the signs in the bracket are different; the bigger number in the bracket has the same sign as a.

EXAMPLE 1

Solve the equation $x^2 - 4x + 3 = 0$.

$(x - 3)(x - 1) = 0$ Factorising: both signs are negative, $1 \times 3 = 3$ and $1 + 3 = 4$.

$x - 3 = 0$ or $x - 1 = 0$

The solution is $x = 3$ or $x = 1$.

EXAMPLE 2

Solve the equation $x^2 + 5x + 6 = 0$.

$(x + 3)(x + 2) = 0$ Factorising: both signs are positive, $2 \times 3 = 6$ and $2 + 3 = 5$.

$x + 3 = 0$ or $x + 2 = 0$

The solution is $x = {}^-3$ or $x = {}^-2$.

EXAMPLE 3

Solve the equation $x^2 - 3x - 10 = 0$.

$(x - 5)(x + 2) = 0$ Factorising: the signs are different, $5 \times 2 = 10$ and $5 - 2 = 3$.

$x - 5 = 0$ or $x + 2 = 0$

The solution is $x = 5$ or $x = {}^-2$.

If an equation is written as $x^2 - 2x = 15$ or $x^2 = 2x + 15$, first rearrange it so that all the terms are on one side, leaving zero on the other side.

STAGE

8

EXAMPLE 4

Solve the equation $x^2 = 4x - 4$ by factorisation.

$x^2 - 4x + 4 = 0$ Rearrange so that all the terms are on the same side.
$(x - 2)(x - 2) = 0$ Factorising: the signs are both negative, $2 \times 2 = 4$, $2 + 2 = 4$.

$x - 2 = 0$ or $x - 2 = 0$

The solution is $x = 2$ (repeated).

There are always two answers, so if they are both the same write 'repeated'.

EXAMPLE 5

Solve the equation $x^2 + 5x = 0$.

$x(x + 5) = 0$ Factorising with x as a common factor.

$x = 0$ or $x + 5 = 0$

The solution is $x = 0$ or $x = {}^-5$.

EXAMPLE 6

Solve the equation $x^2 - 49 = 0$.

$(x + 7)(x - 7) = 0$ Factorising by 'difference of two squares'.
$x + 7 = 0$ or $x - 7 = 0$
The solution is $x = {}^-7$ or $x = 7$.   This can be written $x = \pm 7$.

An alternative method is

$x^2 - 49 = 0$
$x^2 = 49$ Adding 49 to both sides.
$x = \pm 7$ Taking the square root of both sides, remembering that this can give 7 or $^-7$.

This method is perhaps simpler but it is easy to forget the negative solution.

EXERCISE 19.1

Solve these equations by factorisation.

1   $x^2 - 5x + 6 = 0$

2   $x^2 - 7x + 10 = 0$

3   $x^2 - 6x + 5 = 0$

4   $x^2 - 4x + 3 = 0$

5   $x^2 - 16 = 0$

6   $x^2 - 100 = 0$

7   $x^2 + 6x + 8 = 0$

8   $x^2 - 8x + 15 = 0$

9   $x^2 + 5x + 4 = 0$

10   $x^2 + 9x + 20 = 0$

11   $x^2 - 7x = 0$

12   $x^2 - 25 = 0$

13   $x^2 + 2x + 1 = 0$

14   $x^2 + 7x + 6 = 0$

15   $x^2 - 7x + 6 = 0$

16   $x^2 - 9x + 18 = 0$

17   $x^2 - 1 = 0$

18   $x^2 - 8x = 0$

19   $x^2 - 7x + 10 = 0$

20   $x^2 + 7x + 12 = 0$

21   $x^2 - 4x + 3 = 0$

22   $x^2 - 2x + 1 = 0$

23   $x^2 + 3x = 0$

24   $x^2 + 6x = 0$

25   $x^2 - 9x + 14 = 0$

26   $x^2 - 10x + 24 = 0$

27   $x^2 - 6x + 8 = 0$

28   $x^2 + 4x + 3 = 0$

29   $x^2 - 169 = 0$

30   $x^2 - 225 = 0$

31   $x^2 - 2x - 8 = 0$

32   $x^2 + 2x - 3 = 0$

33   $x^2 + 4x - 5 = 0$

34   $x^2 + 3x - 10 = 0$

35   $x^2 = 10x$

36   $x^2 = 5x$

37   $x^2 - x - 6 = 0$

38   $x^2 - x - 12 = 0$

39   $x^2 + 5x - 6 = 0$

40   $x^2 + 5x - 14 = 0$

41   $x^2 = x$

42   $x^2 = 3x$

43   $x^2 + 2x = 3$

44   $x^2 - 2x - 15 = 0$

45   $x^2 - 3x = 18$

46   $x^2 - 3x - 28 = 0$

EXERCISE 19.1 continued

47 $x^2 - 9x = 10$

48 $x^2 - 17x + 30 = 0$

49 $x^2 + 9x + 14 = 0$

50 $x^2 + 4x = 32$

51 $x^2 + 9x - 22 = 0$

52 $x^2 + 9x = 36$

53 $x^2 + x - 12 = 0$

54 $x^2 + x = 20$

CHALLENGE 1

I think of a number. I add 6 to it. I multiply the result by the original number and add 3. The answer is 58.

Write down an equation and solve it to find the original number.

CHALLENGE 2

The diagram shows a rectangular pen made of fencing on three sides and a wall on the fourth side.

a) If 50 m of fencing is used, find the length of the pen in terms of x.

b) If the area of the pen is 272 m², write down an equation in x and show that it simplifies to

$x^2 - 25x + 136 = 0$.

c) Solve your equation to find the length and width of the pen.

STAGE

8

CHALLENGE 3

The area of the triangle is $18\,cm^2$.

a) Write down an equation in x and simplify it.

b) Hence solve the equation to find the lengths AB and BC.

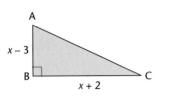

Rearranging formulae

All the formulae that you have rearranged previously contained the new subject only once, and also the subject was not raised to a power. This is now extended in the following examples.

▌▌ EXAMPLE 7

Rearrange the formula $A = \pi r^2$ to make r the subject.

$A = \pi r^2$

$\dfrac{A}{\pi} = r^2$ Divide both sides by π.

$r^2 = \dfrac{A}{\pi}$ Rearrange to get all terms involving r on the left-hand side.

$r = \sqrt{\dfrac{A}{\pi}}$ Take the square root of both sides.

> **EXAM TIP**
> The negative squre root is not required because r is a length.

▌▌ EXAMPLE 8

Rearrange the formula $V = \frac{4}{3}\pi r^3$ to make r the subject.

$3V = 4\pi r^3$ Multiply both sides by 3.

$4\pi r^3 = 3V$ Rearrange to get all terms involving r on the left-hand side

$r^3 = \dfrac{3V}{4\pi}$ Divide both sides by 4π.

$r = \sqrt[3]{\dfrac{3V}{4\pi}}$ Take the cube root of both sides.

STAGE

8

EXAMPLE 9

Rearrange the formula $a = x + \dfrac{cx}{d}$ to make x the subject.

$ad = dx + cx$	Multiply both sides by d.
$dx + cx = ad$	Rearrange to get all terms involving x (the subject) on the left-hand side.
$x(d + c) = ad$	Factorise the left-hand side, taking out the factor x.
$x = \dfrac{ad}{d + c}$	Divide both sides by the bracket $(d + c)$.

EXAMPLE 10

Rearrange the equation $ax + by = cy - ad$ to make a the subject.

$ax + ad = cy - by$	Rearrange to get all terms involving a on the left-hand side and all the other terms on the right-hand side. This is done by adding ad to both sides and subtracting by from both sides.
$a(x + d) = cy - by$	Factorise the left-hand side, taking out the factor a.
$a = \dfrac{cy - by}{x + d}$	Divide both sides by the bracket $(x + d)$.

EXERCISE 19.2

For questions **1** to **20**, make the letter shown in brackets the subject.

1	$s = at + 2bt$	(t)	**5**	$A = 4\pi r^2$	(r)
2	$s = ab - bc$	(b)	**6**	$3(a + y) = by + 7$	(y)
3	$P = t - \dfrac{at}{b}$	(t)	**7**	$ab - cd = ac$	(a)
4	$v^2 = u^2 + 2as$	(u)	**8**	$2(a - 1) = b(1 - 2a)$	(a)

9 $ab - cd = ac$ (c)

10 $\dfrac{a}{b} - 2a = b$ (a)

11 $s - 2ax = b(x - s)$ (s)

12 $s = 2r^2 - 1$ (r)

13 $s - 2ax = b(x - s)$ (x)

14 $a(b + d) = c(b - d)$ (d)

15 $a = \dfrac{t}{b} - st$ (t)

16 $a(b + d) = c(b - d)$ (b)

17 $a = b + c^2$ (c)

18 $V = 5ab^2 + 3c^3$ (c)

19 $A = P + \dfrac{PRT}{100}$ (P)

20 $s = \dfrac{uv}{u + v}$ (v)

21 The formula for the volume of a cylinder is $V = \pi r^2 h$, where r is the radius of the cylinder and h is its height.
  a) Find the volume of a cylinder of radius 12 cm and height 20 cm. Give your answer to 2 significant figures.
  b) Rearrange the formula to make r the subject.
  c) What is the radius of a cylinder of volume 500 cm^3 and height 5 cm? Give your answer to 3 significant figures.

22 The formula for finding the length, d, of the diagonal of a cuboid whose dimensions are x, y and z is

$$d = \sqrt{x^2 + y^2 + z^2}.$$

  a) Find d when $x = 2$, $y = 3$ and $z = 4$.
  b) How long is the diagonal of a cuboid block of concrete with dimensions 2 m, 3 m and 75 cm?
  c) Rearrange the formula to make x the subject.
  d) Find x when $d = 0 \cdot 86$ m, $y = 0 \cdot 25$ m, and $z = 0 \cdot 41$ m.

C CHALLENGE 4

Write down the 'formula' you get by following each of these sets of instructions.

a)
- Choose any number.
- Multiply it by two.
- Add five.
- Multiply by five.
- Subtract twenty-five.

b)
- Choose any number.
- Double it.
- Add nine.
- Add the original number.
- Divide by three.
- Subtract three.

What answer do you get for each set if your starting number is ten?

STAGE

8

C CHALLENGE 5

The formula for the surface area of a closed cylinder is $A = 2\pi r(r + h)$, where r is the radius of the cylinder and h is its height.

What happens if you try to make r the subject?

K KEY IDEAS

■ To solve a quadratic equation, first rearrange the equation, if necessary, so that all the terms are on the left-hand side and leaving zero on the other side. Then factorise the left-hand side and set each bracket equal to zero to find the two solutions.

■ To rearrange a formula where the subject occurs twice, first rearrange the formula so that all the terms containing the subject are on one side and all the other terms are on the other. Then take the subject out as a common factor. Finally divide by the other factor.

■ To rearrange a formula where the subject (r) is squared, first make r^2 the subject, then find the square root of both sides. If the subject is cubed then find the cube root.

STAGE

8

Revision exercise E1

1 Multiply out these brackets and simplify your answers.
- **a)** $(x + 3)(x + 9)$
- **b)** $(y - 6)(y + 7)$
- **c)** $(a - 8)^2$
- **d)** $(b - 2)(b - 10)$
- **e)** $(p + 10)(p - 3)$
- **f)** $(a + 9)(a - 9)$
- **g)** $(a + 9)^2$
- **h)** $(x - 20)(x - 1)$

2 Factorise these.
- **a)** $x^2 + 5x + 4$
- **b)** $x^2 - 6x + 8$
- **c)** $x^2 - 10x + 16$
- **d)** $x^2 + 8x + 15$
- **e)** $x^2 - 6x - 7$
- **f)** $x^2 - 3x - 10$
- **g)** $x^2 - 8x + 12$
- **h)** $x^2 - 2x - 15$
- **i)** $x^2 - 3x - 70$
- **j)** $x^2 + 16x + 48$
- **k)** $x^2 - 7x - 18$
- **l)** $x^2 + 8x - 20$

3 Factorise these.
- **a)** $a^2 - 64$
- **b)** $x^2 - 9$
- **c)** $p^2 - 100$
- **d)** $x^2 - 196$

4 The table shows the number of people unemployed at the end of each quarter in a county to the nearest 100.
The months indicate the end of the quarter for which the figures are given.

	January	April	July	October
2002	41 700	38 300	35 600	33 100
2003	33 800	28 500	24 600	23 500
2004	26 600	24 000	22 200	21 100
2005	23 800	20 900	18 900	17 700

- **a)** Plot these figures in a graph.
  Use a scale of 1 cm to each quarter on the horizontal axis and 2 cm to 10 000 people on the vertical axis.
- **b)** Calculate the four-quarter moving averages.
- **c)** Plot the moving averages on your graph.
- **d)** Comment on the general trend and the quarterly variation.

5 The table shows the daily absences from a school over a four-week period.

	M	Tu	W	Th	F
Week 1	52	38	33	37	46
Week 2	48	33	29	28	41
Week 3	46	28	30	25	35
Week 4	39	25	23	21	29

- **a)** Plot a time-series graph of these figures.
  Use a scale of 1 cm to each day on the horizontal axis and 2 cm to 10 people on the vertical axis.
- **b)** Calculate the five-day moving averages.
- **c)** Plot the moving averages on your graph.
- **d)** Comment on the general trend and the daily variation.

6 The table shows the number of people visiting a leisure centre each day for a four-week period.

	Su	M	Tu	W	Th	F	Sa
Week 1	1037	542	731	1084	832	905	1617
Week 2	1405	741	750	905	794	927	1392
Week 3	1605	763	801	928	937	1017	1854
Week 4	2047	694	728	861	904	935	1532

a) Plot a time-series graph of these figures. Use a scale of 1 cm to 2 days on the horizontal axis and 1 cm to 100 people on the vertical axis. (You can start the y-axis at 500.)

b) Calculate the seven-day moving averages.

c) Plot the moving averages on your graph.

d) Comment on the general trend and the daily variation.

7 Solve these quadratic equations.
a) $x^2 - 6x + 8 = 0$
b) $x^2 + 5x + 6 = 0$
c) $x^2 - 2x - 3 = 0$
d) $x^2 - 3x - 10 = 0$
e) $x^2 - 5x + 4 = 0$
f) $x^2 + 7x + 10 = 0$
g) $x^2 - 5x - 14 = 0$
h) $x^2 + 17x + 30 = 0$
i) $x^2 - 9x + 20 = 0$
j) $x^2 + 4x + 3 = 0$
k) $x^2 - 9x - 36 = 0$
l) $x^2 + 7x - 18 = 0$

8 Solve these quadratic equations.
a) $x^2 + 8x = 0$
b) $x^2 - 5x = 0$
c) $x^2 = 64$
d) $x^2 - 100 = 0$
e) $x^2 = 10x$
f) $x^2 - 4x = 5$
g) $x^2 + 2x = 8$
h) $x^2 = 8x + 9$

9 Make the letter shown in brackets the subject of these formulae.
a) $x = by + a^2$ (a)
b) $y = x + ay$ (y)
c) $ab - cd = bx$ (b)
d) $ab + cd = ac - bd$ (b)
e) $A = b^3 + 3c^2d$ (b)
f) $A = ab + \dfrac{\pi a}{2}$ (a)
g) $3(x - 5) = y(4 - 3x)$ (x)
h) $V = \pi r^2 h$ (r)
i) $3(x - y) = 4(x + 2ay)$ (y)
j) $P = 3t - 5s^2$ (s)
k) $\dfrac{1}{u} + \dfrac{1}{v} = \dfrac{1}{f}$ (u)

10 The formula $V = \frac{2}{3}\pi r^3$ gives the volume of a hemisphere. Where necessary, give your answers to 3 significant figures.

a) Find the volume of a hemisphere with a radius of 8 cm.

b) Make r the subject of the formula $V = \frac{2}{3}\pi r^3$.

c) Find the radius of a hemisphere with a volume of 5000 cm³.

Index

STAGE
8